P R A I S E   F

THIS TROUBLED ～...～ ‑

"In *This Troubled Ground*, Les Carroll delivers deep insight into the Afghanistan War, which, though fought for many years, still baffles Americans as they ask themselves, 'Was it really worth the cost?' Showing us examples of how quickly single events can escalate into life-and-death situations, Carroll offers the reader a unique view of this war, which was fought like no other.

"Knowing the exorbitant personal cost all too well, I can personally confirm that Les Carroll's details of the Dover experience will send cold shivers down the spine. The Dover experience was indeed a beautiful ceremony, yet full of absolute horror. I wailed when I was there, and I sobbed again each time Carroll's stirring narrative took me back to my few minutes on the ramp at Dover."

—Diane Rawl, Gold Star Mother of 1LT Ryan Rawl, Killed in Afghanistan June 20, 2012

"This novel is Les Carroll at his very best, capturing the real price of freedom and the impact of war on those who serve and their families. His firsthand experience of the effects of war truly breathes life into the oft quoted 'All gave some and some gave all.'"

—Brigadier General (Ret.) Calvin H. Elam, US Air Force

"Lt. Col. Les Carroll's book *This Troubled Ground* portrays the sights, sounds, and emotions that all service members share when deployed overseas. His words are moving and poignant. Once I started reading the book, I was flooded with memories from my own deployments, and I couldn't put it down."

—Major General (Ret.) Barry K. Coln, US Air Force

"*This Troubled Ground* is an emotionally powerful book that offers insight into the courageous sacrifices made by men and women at war and their unwavering commitment to bringing hope to those in need. It sheds light on the little-known but highly respected task of the Dignified Transfer Team, part of the US Armed Forces, who honor fallen heroes and their families with the utmost reverence.

"Les Carroll is a craftsman who skillfully weaves narratives from his duties as part of the Dignified Transfer Team and his two deployments in Afghanistan. . . .

"*This Troubled Ground* poses a timeless and universal question about America's twenty-year combat operation in Afghanistan. Was the war worth the overwhelming cost of human lives? It is a question that families of the fallen ask repeatedly, and it deserves our collective consideration as Americans.

"*This Troubled Ground* is a must-read. Once you start, you will not put it down until it's finished—and then you will breathe again."

—Brigadier General (Ret.) Marie Goff, United States Army

"Several years ago, I had the honor of playing Colonel Frank Sherwood on the television show *Army Wives*. I met Les Carroll when he came aboard as a military adviser for the show. We became friends, and I grew to value his sense of duty, intelligence, and deep compassion.

"It is with the deeply humane heart of a father, husband, and soldier that, with this gut-wrenching novel memoir *This Troubled Ground*, Les recalls the honor and duty of his service at Dover AFB, supporting the dignified transfers of one hundred American warfighters, while grappling with the seemingly unknowable reasons why many of our country's young men and women gave their lives in Afghanistan.

"From his first, eye-opening transport through the war-torn ruins of Kabul to his bittersweet goodbye to compatriots and friends, Carroll's open heart is worn on his sleeve next to the American flag and ISAF insignia.

"This account of his service in Afghanistan and at Dover AFB offers a compelling look behind the walls of the US mission in Afghanistan and the blood and treasure sacrificed upon its dubious conclusion."

—Terry Serpico, Emmy and SAG Awards–Nominated Television and Film Actor *(Law & Order: SVU, Yellowstone, Army Wives, Homeland)*

This Troubled Ground
by Les Carroll

Published by

◤ köehlerbooks™

3705 Shore Drive
Virginia Beach, VA 23455
800–435–4811
www.koehlerbooks.com

THIS
TROUBLED
GROUND

A NOVEL

LES CARROLL

VIRGINIA BEACH
CAPE CHARLES

CHAPTER 1

A FREEZING, CUTTING wind whipped across the Dover tarmac, straight into my face. I braced myself against the blast, tried to stand completely still—at perfect attention—but fought my own body's relentless shivering and teeth chattering. I glanced to my immediate right at the family area, where chaplains and their assistants, military escorts, and mortuary specialists encircled grieving parents, really young wives—now widows—and heartbroken siblings. The whole group sequestered themselves in the heavy shadows cast by the shiny blue surrey bus. The family members' support staff seemed locked into place against the soft barrier I had constructed a few minutes earlier by hooking the blue nylon belts between silver-based stanchions. I shot my eyes left, memorized the position of the four news media representatives, made sure I was positioned correctly between the media and any view they might have of the family, should any enterprising journalist out to make a name for himself consider violating the strict prohibition against photographing family members. Everything was in perfect order, again. *What number was this?* I had to be pushing ninety dignified transfers by now. Not ninety different days or nights on the ramp, but ninety fallen service members and a decision on whether to allow media coverage made by ninety different family members.

Just in front of me, the extended flatbed from a K-loader butted against the rear fuselage door of the 747 jumbo jet. In the doorway a flag-draped transfer case rested in stationary solitude. It was both a symbol and a reality—another young hero lost, a harsh reminder to the family just to my right that we were not only a country at war, but their son, husband, and brother, had died for our country. He had been cut to pieces by an improvised explosive device planted shallow in a roadside by a poor Afghan who had taken a few bucks of food money from the enemy insurgent. Afghanistan had forged a distinct place in my own personal history, recollections of having been there passing through my mind constantly as I stood on the frozen Dover tarmac. I remembered without trying very hard almost two hundred days and nights that had bridged the previous two years, more questions than answers on my lips at the conclusion of those two hundred days. Afghanistan haunted me. I let a very short memory pass through my mind while I stood shivering and waiting for the ceremony I now had memorized.

Kabul, Afghanistan October 30, 2008

I got my first real look at Afghanistan from a UH-60 Blackhawk on a quick flight from Bagram to Kabul International Airport. Below me, Afghanistan looked like a flat brown rug with odd-shaped objects trapped beneath. The compounds below puzzled me, and I could actually see people moving about inside their walls. I wondered what life must be like down there.

The massive plane rested heavy on the Dover ramp. Just inside the aircraft doorway, a half dozen Air Force and Marine Corps officers and enlisted men and women stood at attention. Then the six-member Marine Corps carry team emerged from inside the plane, lined up on each side of the metal transfer case and formed a protective human shield around the rectangular flag-draped box, which contained the disfigured body of a nineteen-year-old lance corporal killed instantly thirty hours earlier by one of those previously described roadside bombs. Moments earlier, an Air Force major—a chaplain—then an Air Force colonel, and a Marine

Corps colonel had marched across the peripheral view on my left, their movements not quite so crisp as the carry team before them. They had climbed the stairs, disappeared for a full minute, then reappeared in the rear cargo doorway of the mammoth aircraft just ahead of the carry team. The three officers took their places at the head of the transfer case. They bowed their heads. The carry team, the support team, and participating aircrew members in makeshift formation on the plane bowed their heads, and the chaplain started to pray. I bowed my head, although I couldn't clearly hear his words. Every few seconds I stole a surreptitious glance at the group gathered around the transfer case, then the family to my right. The journalists kept working, albeit quietly and with less push than usual.

To us on the ground the prayer was drowned out by the muffled sobbing of a grieving mother. The prayer was quieted even more by white noise near and far, the sometimes nerve-shredding, staccato ticking of aircraft engine blades still turning inside their housing, perpetually propelled by the robust wind. There was other movement on the ramp several hundred yards from us, cargo being loaded and unloaded, generators humming, the engine of a C-5 just coming to life for the sortie to follow. But I stood motionless, the Associated Press and Air Force photographers to my left and family members to my right.

The prayer complete, the carry team lifted the case and moved it to the end of the K-loader, every pointed-toe step a bitter reminder of the precious cargo they carried. The loader swayed back and forth gently as the team members reached their mark, marched in place, and then came to a unified halt. They lowered the case with the same care, knelt beside it, paused in tribute, then slid it carefully until the foot of the case was flush with the end of the K-loader. When they retreated back into the airplane, the flag-draped case rested in complete solitude on the edge of the loader and the heartbroken mother sobbed louder. She was joined by other family members.

This was the break in the event that gave me a chance to close my eyes and go away from the surreal for a few moments. Sometimes I just needed to get away, think of the life I left behind, or the one ahead. It was a welcomed break in the middle of what sometimes felt like the most solemn and longest ten minutes of my life. I had vowed not to let it become commonplace—ever—even after I'd seen nearly a hundred flag-draped cases carried off aircraft of different sizes, colors, and types. Some were Air Force planes—C-17s and C-5s—and others were commercial carriers, mostly 747s and the occasional DC-8 or something like it.

I opened my eyes again, just in time to see the official party and the marines of the carry team take their places across from each other on the tarmac, almost directly under the aircraft's left wing. The K-loader roared to a start and the platform and transfer case slowly lowered. The sobbing of the family intensified with every foot downward the case descended. I could sense the mother was actually trying to control her emotions, refrain from the type of outbursts and meltdowns we had experienced before. But still, she continued to cry as the case passed her eye level. The K-loader reached ground level, the operator cut the engine, and there was again an eerie quiet in the immediate area that seemed to block out the noise of the engine blades and the distant flightline operations. Now I could actually hear the mother asking questions through her sobs, but I couldn't make out her words. The marines eased out of their static formation, marched forward four paces, executed a crisp left face, marched to the end of the loader, and took up their positions. The team leader stepped between them, gripped the handles of the case, and pulled it toward him. As he stepped back, the team members latched on, distributing the weight evenly among them. The stalwart marines lifted the case and held it steady. The call to present arms by the Air Force colonel rose suddenly, like sound coming from nowhere in particular. The Air Force captain echoed the command from inside the plane, a shadowed voice that seemed to emit from a dark cave.

"Preeesent..."

"Preeesent," came the echo from inside the airplane.

"Arms!"

The carry team leader worked his command to *forward march* into the pauses in the colonel's call to present arms. The military members raised their right arms slowly in the solemn, ceremonial salute. I saluted, looked past my raised hand to the family viewing area, and stole a quick glance at grieving loved ones who huddled closely against the cutting wind. The Marine Corps carry team stepped out in perfect unison and the cameras to my left snapped relentlessly. The thirty-foot walk to the transfer vehicle seemed to take a long time, and every second was painful to watch. The team reached the vehicle, placed the flag-draped case onto the vehicle's rollers and the case disappeared. The colonel called out *order arms*. The team turned and took five calculated paces away from the vehicle, executed their unique countermarch, and stopped behind the vehicle. The airman—cleverly referred to as the TV guide (transfer vehicle guide)—closed the doors. The TV guide repositioned herself behind the vehicle, the colonel called *present arms*, and the vehicle eased forward. The colonel called *order arms* and the carry team moved in behind the vehicle, followed by the TV guide and then the official party. The transfer vehicle rolled slowly down the tarmac's perimeter road. I turned to face it. The photographers captured their final images, and their cameras went silent and still.

The family members turned, huddled, stared at the vehicle's gradual retreat. The dignified transfer over, the mourning would continue. The vehicle disappeared into the black night long before the pinpoints of the red taillights. The family stayed huddled until the red lights disappeared. We stood at parade rest and waited. It took three or four more minutes for the family to breathe again and accept closure on this chapter of their nightmare. Finally, reluctantly, they climbed back on the bus and departed. I and my team could finally breathe again too, but we remained subdued in our movement until the rear bus lights disappeared behind a distant building. Then we moved into our postevent ritual, stacking the orange cones and retracting the nylon lines into their stanchions. We loaded our gear into the back of the van, pushed our cameras and tripods behind the cones and stanchions, and slammed the doors shut. The media loaded back into their vehicle and quickly departed the tarmac. Another mission complete, but I wondered if we were allowing this process to become routine. Only a handful of people in the world performed this important mission. It was not routine, and I reminded myself of that . . . a lot! It was not routine this time, or would it be the next time. For every family this was the worst moment of their lives. There was nothing routine about this night, even though it was just like every other night.

Later, back at the mortuary public affairs office, my deputy, Captain Needham, and I started peeling off the layers of cold-weather gear.

"It was freakin' cold out there tonight," I said.

"Gonna be worse tomorrow night. Wind chill's gonna be around zero," the captain replied.

"Holy crap."

The NCOs, Sergeants Tony Deguire and Kate Shearman, dragged themselves and their gear through the door. I snatched Sergeant Shearman's tripod, shoved it into a corner.

"Sir, there's no need to shove that in the corner. Looks like we're going to need it again in a few hours," she said.

"Probably."

I backed into my small corner cubicle, guided my military ID card into the reader slot, and typed in my PIN. There were a dozen highlighted new email messages. I clicked on the first with the subject *Inbound HR*. Click. Click. The attachment opened. Click and click. I walked back to the front of the office and pulled a single sheet of paper off the printer.

"Two more on the board," I said.

"When?" Deguire asked.

"Tomorrow, late."

I picked up the red dry erase marker and faced the white board, then started filling in the information.

2 x USMC

Date: 22 Feb

Time: 2120

Then I wrote two names and additional information.

L.Cpl Groberg—Full Media—Orlando, FL

L.Cpl Jones—Media TBD—Pittsburgh, PA

"What time in the morning, sir?"

I thought about it for a moment, calculated some times in my mind.

"Let's make it ten."

Needham, Shearman, and Deguire gathered their things quickly and exited. I returned to my computer, brought up the internet search engine and typed in the name, Lance Corporal Zach Groberg. I clicked on a news article from the *Orlando Sentinel*. There was his high school senior photo. It's like I was looking at the real kid up close—star quarterback, Eagle Scout. He was the all-American kid that everyone liked.

"He treated everyone the same, whether you were the homecoming queen or the shyest kid in the school," his high school principal had said. "He was a friend to everyone. That always impressed me, because he was one of the most popular kids in the school, but he treated everyone with kindness and respect."

I stared at the words for another half minute—the brightest star in his community had been extinguished by a roadside bomb in Afghanistan, probably placed by a poor Afghan farmer who needed the hundred dollars the Taliban had paid him to feed his family. Sometimes I wanted to hate those people when I looked at the faces of families, like Zach Groberg's, whom I would see on the ramp the next night. It was easy to hate the Taliban but what about that poor farmer? I closed the search and snatched my military ID card from its slot in the keyboard.

Back in my room at the lodging building, I turned on my personal notebook computer and started typing. This was where I could feel something and put what I felt in several running journals I had kept since arriving here three months earlier. I wrote the names of the fallen service members whose dignified transfers I had witnessed. Then I wrote what I knew about them, what I was feeling, and what impact this job was having on me. At the office we had our job to do, and sometimes young marines—the brightest stars in their families, schools, and communities—became names and numbers, taskings for me and my team. When I sat in the solitude of my third-floor room, I could think about these young people and try to see them, bring back for a moment the young lives extinguished by war.

The weather the next night was near zero wind chill, but my team was not on the ramp. The aircraft bringing home the body of Lance Corporal Zach Groberg was delayed twenty-four hours because of inclement weather in Germany. Another night and day for his family to sit in a nearby hotel and grieve, while asking aloud and to themselves the same question—why?

The following night, the plane arrived and landed just ahead of an advancing warm front pushing in a weird winter thunderstorm. By the time we got on the ramp for the dignified transfer, the bitterly cold temperatures had turned into a blinding, freezing rainstorm. I got out of our staff van and set up the family area for the DT. The media van arrived, and Needham got out with an Associated Press photographer and a Washington-based TV crew, who set up beside Sergeant Deguire's camera. They pointed their lenses toward the plane, a C-17. Straight out from the rear ramp of the aircraft the transfer vehicle waited. It actually rocked back and forth as the wind cut across it. The transfer vehicle guide—the airmen who shut the doors after the remains were loaded into the vehicle—shivered beside the back doors of the van.

Finally, the family arrived by van, and I marshaled it in, parked it parallel to the aircraft fuselage. I stood near the front bumper of the small surrey and glanced to my right as the occupants began to come off the bus reluctantly. The funeral director exited the bus first, pulled his collar tightly around his neck, walked in front of the bus to me and extended his hand. We shook hands and his grip was firm and warm. When he let go of my hand and stepped back, I realized my hands were freezing already, and the DT had not yet started.

The chaplains and their assistants, then military escorts, came off the bus behind the funeral director. Finally, I saw the young parents of Zach Groberg, then his nineteen-year-old widow, the childhood sweetheart of the star quarterback. She fell into the arms of her father-in-law and started sobbing, then strained to see up into the airplane, where just part of the transfer case was visible. During the dignified transfer, I closed my eyes. Zach Groberg came back to life in my mind. I envisioned an imaginary scene, the young marine as a star high school quarterback, after the big game. He smiled broadly, celebrated with his teammates, hugged his cute cheerleader girlfriend, now the shocked teenaged widow. Then he high fived the unpopular kid, the geek whom the other jocks had stuffed into a trashcan just for fun, until Zach Groberg told them it wasn't cool to pick on the weak kid, adding that the football players should stick up for the geeks and little kids who couldn't defend themselves. I don't know if it happened like that, but there are young people like that in this country, so I'd wanted to believe Zach Groberg was one of them. I liked this young man, Zach Gro—*Boom!* I was shaken from my quick dream when the colonel called *present arms.*

When the DT was over, the red-faced teenage widow climbed back on the bus before everyone else. She didn't linger behind in denial, watching the transfer vehicle slowly disappear into the night. She returned to her seat on the left side of the bus, facing forward, looking out. I maneuvered to the side of bus near her so I could keep the transfer vehicle in site. I stood at attention but turned my head slightly in her direction. She was staring at me. Her lips moved. I don't know what she was trying to say, but I mouthed the words "I'm sorry." I think she understood because she nodded her head ever so slightly. I thought moments after she was gone that she might've mouthed the words "why did this happen?" It had been a long and uncomfortable half minute, but thirty more seconds I would not forget.

Back in the van, I warmed my hands by the dashboard heater. Deguire climbed in, took the wheel and we slowly rolled across the frozen tarmac.

"That was a tough one," Deguire said as we drove.

"You're going to do about a hundred more."

"Is that how many you've done?" he asked.

"I'm over ninety now, I think," I said, "something like that. Plus we supported the seven CIA officers killed in Afghanistan."

"Bet that was interesting."

"Oh yeah. It was one of the worst days, emotionally. No media, but about a hundred and fifty family members and a couple hundred CIA staffers and leadership."

"Shit."

"Yep. Lots of kids, and we were right beside them," I continued. "We weren't segregated from the families like tonight. We were right in the middle of the group."

"Wow."

"Met Leon Panetta and General Cartwright."

The planning for that dignified transfer had taken place on New Year's Day. Around mid-morning the colonel had told me to show up at the office at noon, in uniform. I arrived thirty minutes early and waited in our team room for more than an hour, then later started watching a very uninspired University of South Carolina football team get their asses kicked in some obscure bowl game. At halftime of the game, coincidentally, an entourage of CIA officers and support staff, led by a very confident woman, marched into the mortuary's front offices to brief us on exactly how the director—that would be Leon Panetta, former White House chief of staff—wanted, rather expected the dignified transfer of his seven CIA officers (they are referred to as officers, not agents, we were told) to be planned, managed, and executed in two days. What would become one of the most memorable days of my life unfolded exactly as he had dictated. It had been a bitter cold day, made more uncomfortable by a lively, sweeping wind that raced across the tarmac. I had stood just feet from the husband and children of the woman who had led the team in Afghanistan. The solemnity of the moment was unsettled by the cries of crushed family members, rocked by the shocking realization that the metal containers coming off the aircraft contained the shredded remains of their loved ones—moms and dads, wives and husbands, daughters and sons, sisters and brothers.

Then a day after the DT, as if I were always in the wrong—or maybe right—place, I was standing by the front desk when the husband and young daughter of the CIA team leader, who had died along with seven others in a surprise suicide attack by a Jordanian doctor the agents thought was on their side, walked into the Air Force Mortuary Affairs Operations (AFMAO) lobby. The daughter had picked out the dress she wanted her mother buried in, so I took the bag and delivered it to the mortuary staff in the back of the house. I later saw the CIA agent in that dress, just hours before her family took custody of her for the private funeral service she had actually planned in advance—just in case she came home the way she came home. I was back in Afghanistan three years later when the movie *Zero Dark Thirty* exploded into our world. I watched it alone late one night in my room, and it was like I had been there, like I knew her. She was a real person, not just a character in that movie. She had a name, different from, but similar to, the character portrayed in the movie by American actress Jennifer Ehle.

After Zach Groberg's return to American soil, I would not have known there had been nearly one hundred dignified transfers except that I had made a count a few days earlier. I knew I was near a hundred, so I added them all up. I came up with a number, but even alone, I felt guilty for tallying a number. It didn't seem like almost a hundred, but as I scanned the list of names, I remembered most of them, some better than others. But all had affected me in some way. During the early weeks I had strictly obeyed the instructions from my predecessor to stand at attention and avoid any eye contact with grieving family members. But in time those instructions began to seem unnecessary. I didn't stare at family members or intentionally make eye contact with them, but I didn't avoid them. And so some experiences stood out in my mind, like that cold, dark night when Lance Corporal Zach Groberg's widow had climbed back on the bus, then turned in her seat to look out the window.

I had only spoken to three family members during my Dover deployment, four if I counted the nonverbal communication with the teenaged widow. One was the sister-in-law of a fallen US Marine. She called my office four hours before the dignified transfer to make sure she would be allowed to attend. I looked at the dignified transfer information card in front of me and saw her name listed.

"You're on the family list," I told her. "That means your sister has told the Army liaison here that you are invited to attend the DT."

"His wife is not my sister. My ex-husband is his brother. She hates me, so I wasn't sure I would be allowed to attend."

"You're on the list."

"I'm actually surprised," she added. "Maybe it takes a tragedy to bring about forgiveness."

We talked about what would happen during the dignified transfer.

"This is very bad for our whole family," she said.

"It's been a bad week," I responded. Her brother-in-law was one of six US Marines to fall in Afghanistan that week, along with five soldiers of the US Army.

"It's time to get our men and women out of there," she said.

"I don't know," I said.

"I'm sorry. I can get a little opinionated sometimes."

"It's fine."

"That's why she hates me."

"I'm sure she doesn't hate you. It's just—"

"No, she hates me."

I spent almost two hundred days in Afghanistan but felt I only possessed a simple and rudimentary understanding of the NATO and US mission there—to rid the country of terrorism and restore some sense of stability. Build the Afghan National Security Forces. Deny safe havens for terrorists so we don't have another 9/11. I had seen some good there. And I knew enough to know that we couldn't bail out of Afghanistan. Too many lives had been lost, too much precious blood spilled to not see it through. It was not the time to try and explain my position to her, but I was glad I didn't react to her statement without thinking. I just wished her well.

Captain Paul Stover's aunt had called, asking for additional photos of the captain's dignified transfer. She had attended with her grieving sister, a single parent who raised an extraordinary son, and sent him from their poor Texas town to West Point where he had become an infantry officer of the United States Army. No mother could ever be prouder. The aunt and I talked for more than an hour. What she didn't know—and I didn't tell her—was that he had been shot in the back by an Afghan interpreter he had dismissed for poor performance, a so-called insider attack or green-on-blue, phrases I would come to understand much better. I recalled one such attack during my first Afghanistan deployment, when a Taliban infiltrator in an Afghan uniform had opened fire on Navy medical officers running on a track inside their forward operating base (FOB). Right then I recalled all the Afghans I had interacted with, worked with, respected and trusted. I also thought—with some trepidation— about times I had stood outside the walls of HQ International Security Assistance Force in Kabul and chatted up Afghan security forces, who sometimes asked me for money. I refused with some joviality, never imagining that any of those young soldiers would consider shooting me in the back when I walked away. During the final days of my first deployment, I had rolled out with three journalists and a company of French soldiers to a FOB in upper Kabul Province, occupied by French troops and a squad-sized unit of Afghan soldiers, who occupied half of the FOB. I had spent so much time with Afghan strangers, and had not realized then, as I knew now, how dangerous that was. I was one of the lucky ones.

Uzbin Valley, Kabul Province, Afghanistan—April 30, 2009
      After the shura, I wandered into the camp of the Afghan National Army soldiers that they shared with marines or soldiers close by—no French. I was completely alone with the Afghans, in their camp, eating their food. Later I played volleyball with some ANA soldiers. Some of them were quite good, as volleyball is very popular here. I ate dinner with them also, which was just naan dipped in the sauce—no rice or lamb. They eat light for dinner. I thought how I couldn't recall seeing an overweight Afghan soldier.

My third encounter with a family member was with the husband of a female Army helicopter pilot who had crashed and died in Iraq. He complained about media being on the ramp, even though he had checked the box during the postnotification briefing that allowed for media coverage. But, I fully intended to give him the benefit of the doubt, knowing he had checked that box an hour or two after hearing that his wife of three years had been cut to pieces in a violent "hard landing" and would not be coming home to him and their one-year-old daughter. When I tried to explain to him that he had agreed to allow media coverage, he lashed out.

      "I didn't know what I was doing when I made that decision," he said through clinched teeth beside the bus door.

      "It's fine, sir. I understand." Wrong choice of words.

      "You *don't* understand. You have no idea what it's like to be told your wife was killed!" My deputy at the time, Lieutenant Shannon Murphy, had stepped into the discussion for me.

"We're just doing our job, sir," she said calmly.

It was a cliché, but it worked. The chaplain coaxed the angry and grieving husband onto the bus.

The calendar reached late February and I was still at Dover. My scheduled departure date from Dover had passed two weeks earlier because my replacement did not show up and three weeks were added to my assignment at the Air Force Mortuary. And it seemed that my extension period got more bizarre and just tougher with every extra day I stayed.

We had hosted a convicted murderer. Private Smith was on his way home, killed by an IED in early February, his return to Dover delayed by the second huge snowstorm of the season. The delay allowed his mother and stepfather to fly all the way from California for the dignified transfer. That also gave the two soldiers en route to Philadelphia International Airport to pick up Private Smith's mother and stepfather, time to read, in astonishment, an unbelievable email sent to them matter-of-factly, the proverbial heads-up, FYI, for your situational awareness, etc. The email read, and I paraphrase: "Just so you know, Private Smith's mother is a convicted murderer, having served sixteen years in prison for her involvement in possibly nine murders committed by the private's father, who died in prison when he was two."

The sergeant had mentioned this to me for my situational awareness, I suppose, and I saw her hours later when they stepped off the bus and onto the tarmac, standing by the stanchions I had set up just for her, to give care, service, and support to the families of the fallen, as our mantra demanded. She didn't look like a serial killer. She was stylishly dressed and attractive, a captivating woman in her fifties. For a murderer, she cleaned up nicely, I thought. That was one dignified transfer at which I did not give the fallen soldier the respect he deserved, because my mind was completely derailed by what I had read and heard about the soldier's mother.

"We've had some interesting families here, to say the least," my deputy deadpanned. "But I believe her story pretty much beats them all."

Yep, I'd say so.

Also, *after* my original departure date, US Forces in Afghanistan had commenced a major offensive on a Taliban stronghold in Helmand Province. Our Department of Defense had actually announced the operation in the media, warned the townspeople to leave and warned the Taliban that a fight was coming. We took the fight to the Taliban with the support of several thousand Afghan National Army soldiers. But the Taliban fought back. Eight fallen US Marines arrived at Dover in the first week of the operation, including four on a sunny, windy Saturday afternoon a week before my eventual departure.

The marines hailed from Virginia, Indiana, Rhode Island, and Pennsylvania, and family and friends poured into the Dover area for the DTs, eventually totaling almost forty. I stood closer than normal because of the way I had positioned the family area and the media. It was a bright day, a rare daytime DT when we could easily see the faces of the family members. I could see the parents of one of the fallen marines, then the wife, parents, and sisters of another. Finally, the family and friends of the nineteen-year-old marine from Pennsylvania piled off the second bus. They had driven in several vehicles from Pennsylvania that morning. The moment they exited the bus and touched the tarmac, the group of male and female young adults could see the flag-draped cases on the aircraft. The crying started immediately, but it was a controlled cry—at first. We had briefed the order the cases would be carried down the aircraft ramp, so the families knew when the case carrying their loved one was in motion. The first case came off, a sergeant from Indiana. I saw his father's arms wrap tighter around his mother and hold her closer. She sucked in her breath and remained composed, almost stoic. Somehow. The second case came off, and the sisters of the corporal broke down, just a sampling of what was to come.

Then the carry team lifted the case of the nineteen-year-old lance corporal from Pennsylvania and started the slow ceremonial march down the ramp of the C-17. The emotions from his family and friends rose and rose. When the carry team reached the flat surface of the tarmac and passed in front of the official party, the emotional outburst reached a frantic crescendo, crying, howling, sobbing. I heard the deep voice of a man call out, but the chaos around the man distorted his words. Then the voice called out again, and this time I heard clearly, "Lucas, I love you son. You're my hero. I love you." I heard sniffling from my team of officers and NCOs standing behind me. I stood firm, but my knees knocked, and my upper body trembled beneath several layers of clothing, the emotion, the bright sunlight, the biting wind hammering away at my military bearing. What had started as a beautiful, chilly Saturday afternoon quickly escalated into the toughest day of my deployment, magnified by the extension of my tour. Now I understood why we were only tasked here for three months. I thought to myself, *This is it. I have to go home now. I can't do this any longer.*

When the fourth case was loaded into the transfer vehicle, the exhausted visitors loaded back onto the buses. When they were gone, the media representatives and my public affairs team remained strangely quiet for the first minute, just going through the motions we had memorized. Needham pushed back tears. He looked like an NFL tight end, but he still struggled not to cry. I trembled inside, and with the family, carry team, and official party off the ramp, I thought maybe I would cry. We stood there for a few more seconds.

"That was tough," I mumbled.

"Sure was," Needham managed.

"It's harder in the daylight," I said. "You can see the family members. They're not just hidden figures buried in the shadows. You hear them and see them."

"You could see me too," he said, "crying like a baby." He lowered his head. "I'm sorry."

"For what? You think I haven't cried out there? If you can stand through that without feeling like your knees are gonna buckle, then you're not breathing."

I nodded to the reporters and photographers, and they climbed back into the van.

Back in the briefing room, the young marines from the carry team sat in the front row of seats. They were not eating pizza this time. Some were pushing back tears. Others looked stunned. They were clearly shaken. The Air Force chaplain stood close by, keeping watch. The Marine Corps lieutenant colonel who had just stood for all four dignified transfers, came walking into the briefing room. He passed me on the way to his men.

"That was a rough one," I said, again.

"Sure was," he said. "I'll get them back to the barracks and give them a few days off, let them unwind."

"Keep an eye on them," the chaplain advised.

"I will," said the lieutenant colonel.

There's that iconic scene in *Saving Private Ryan* where Captain Miller diffuses a tense confrontation between his own men by unloading the close-kept details of his personal life before the war. "I'm a schoolteacher . . ." I give deference to the extraordinary Steven Spielberg, the greatest-of-a-generation actor Tom Hanks, and the brilliant screenwriter Robert Rodat. Just as his men were about to come unhinged from the stresses of war and death all around them, Captain Miller launches into this memorable statement: "Sometimes I wonder if I've changed so much my wife is even going to recognize me whenever it is I get back to her, and how I'll ever be able to tell her about days like today." The fictional captain's soothing speech played quietly in the back of my mind as I walked away from the passenger terminal that day. I had wondered many times during my past Afghanistan deployment, and many times standing on the ramp at Dover Air Force Base—*how will I ever tell my family about days like today?*

CHAPTER TWO

EVERY TIME I noticed Afghanistan or Operation Enduring Freedom on the board in the mortuary operations center, Afghanistan came back alive to me. It had only been a year since I was there. Sometimes it seemed much longer—another lifetime ago, another chapter of my life. Sometimes it seemed like yesterday. Afghanistan and OEF kept appearing on the log board in the operations center, and I got locked in constant recollections.

Kabul, Afghanistan—December 20, 2008

I remember when my children were little we often read a Dr. Seuss book called Oh, the Places You'll Go! I never really thought the good doctor meant me! Just five days before Christmas I boarded a German C-160 with Admiral Borsboom of the Dutch navy and flew to Camp Marmal, the same place I had visited a few weeks earlier. The weather had turned cold and gray. At Kabul International Airport, a group of Afghan National Police recruits huddled outside the passenger terminal trying to stay warm while awaiting their flight to the ANP training facility in Herat. Snow flurries sent a sudden chill through the air, and I noticed they would share their scarves because not everyone had a scarf. One man would use it for a while, then give it to his friend for a few minutes. Many had open-toed shoes—like the Crocs we wore in America for fun—and no socks, thin baggy pants. But, they lined up smartly and enthusiastically when their names were called and their elation was obvious as they moved out, anticipating the days ahead, oblivious to the rigors of the training or the danger of their future jobs, but I'm sure thinking only of the wool coats, thick socks, and warm boots that would be issued and the regular meals that would be served.

So, if I were to write that book, here are the places I could list.

- Australia
- New Zealand
- Canada
- Mexico
- South Korea
- Germany
- East Berlin/West Berlin
- East Germany/West Germany
- Norway
- Denmark
- England
- Ireland
- Austria
- France
- Netherlands
- Belgium
- Luxembourg
- Switzerland
- Italy
- Liechtenstein
- Turkey
- Kyrgyzstan
- Afghanistan—Kabul, Kandahar, Uzbin Valley, Herat, Mazar-e-Sharif, Farah

Maybe that's the whole list.

So, I thought a lot about Dr. Suess books, movies, episodes of Band of Brothers with particularly memorable scenes flashing through my mind, lines from a movie from which I could change a few words and fit it into my little story. I could even remember the names of the Band of Brothers episodes, and one in particular stuck in my mind, "Day of Days."

The following day was one of those days of days. It started with an early morning ride in a German "dingo" this time, a different kind of armored vehicle with seats behind the driver where we sat and could see out. I made my second trip to the Mazar-e-Sharif Provincial Reconstruction Team compound. The Swedish officer briefing the group kept showing pie charts and referred to them as "the cake."

After an hour, we rolled out of there and into MES itself. Just a few weeks earlier I had ridden in the open hatch of another German armored personnel carrier with an animal name—Fox—and had seen Mazar-e-Sharif from a distance. From that vantage point, all I could see was what appeared to be a sleepy and stagnant brown city, spread out flat on the long bench of a hillside. But today we rolled into town like the second coming, and I found something I had not expected, a vibrant and rather boisterous city, alive and relatively prosperous. There are no towns in Afghanistan that I know of that look like antebellum Charleston, South Carolina, or Charlotte, for example. I was in Afghanistan, after all, one of the poorest, most illiterate nations on earth, still surfacing from three decades of war and trying to beat down an insurgency that always reminded us that the quest is difficult, and war was everywhere. But there were some respectable structures, decent roads, shops, cars, homes, gas stations, government buildings, a radio and TV station, car dealerships, and the famous Blue Mosque. Later in the day, on the outskirts, I actually saw large houses—maybe funded by the poppy trade—and what looked like suburbs, if that is even the right phrase for it.

We visited the Mazar-e-Sharif Public Hospital. That was an experience I will never forget. When we rolled onto the grounds of the hospital—again, in an armored convoy— no one really seemed too surprised. I knew these people were accustomed to seeing military vehicles and armed soldiers, but we had to look so completely out of place. The grounds were peaceful, and the people rather laid back. We were still surrounded by menacing walls and had security guards all around us and yet I never once saw a person I thought looked interested in harming me. Everyone we talked to was gracious and appreciative of what we and all the other outsiders were trying to do—to help the people of Afghanistan, and specifically, Mazar-e-Sharif.

On the grounds of the hospital, people hustled past us, the women doing most of the heavy lifting, carrying the children, rushing about. The men mostly strolled around like they had nothing to do and nowhere to go. It was the first time I had really seen burka-draped women up close. They never spoke, and whether they ever looked at me, I had no way of knowing. I did snap a photo of one teenage girl walking beside a woman in a burka. Later, when I looked at the photo and magnified it, I could clearly see that the girl was looking at me as she passed. I remember wondering what she might be thinking.

We visited the Twenty Bed Residential Hospital for Drug Addicts. That's what the sign said, in Dari and English. Admiral Borsboom gave a little pep talk to the resident patients, and they applauded him right before he departed. The pediatric ward was difficult to visit. The conditions were horrible by any standards but would be intolerable by western standards. And the ward was completely staffed by Afghans. In fact, I realized later the whole hospital was staffed by Afghans. There were some very sick children, but they just lay on beds with their mothers beside them, no monitors or machines close by. One little girl lay motionless, her skin a sickening pale blue-green color, and I honestly thought it was a doll, not a real child. The sink was black with dirt and the floor was disgusting.

Later we convoyed to the United Nations field office. We parked and sat stationary in the street for ten minutes. I wouldn't even call it a street. It was more like a muddy alley. The alley was swarming with activities, children playing, a man brewing up some kind of stew on the street. I saw him dip up a cup and hand it to a teenage boy, who gave the old man a coin. I pulled out my camera and started snapping still pictures and recording video, and the kids migrated to the camera. They do love the camera! I felt like I was out there among them, but I was still safely locked up tight in an armored vehicle. I watched them for a long time, and they looked happy. Finally, it was decided that we would egress the vehicle right there in the muddy, potholed alley. The others got out on the right side, toward the building. I climbed out the left side, toward the kids. I jumped down into the mud. They continued to wave, but dared not approach me or this large and ferocious German vehicle called a dingo. I wanted to move right to them, mingle with them, learn something of their lives, but the security personnel had set up a makeshift corridor around the vehicles and us. I looked at one of the armed guards and he motioned to me with just his eyes to move quickly toward the walled compound. Then I was safely inside, imprisoned again by the remote threat of someone out there who might want to hurt me. In the hospital, on these streets, driving through the city, I never once got the impression that anyone out there wanted to hurt me. But, there are people who would. If that were not so, an American soldier would not have died two days later in a firefight with insurgents—and hours later, his family would get the news that their son had lost his life on Christmas Eve trying to bring hope and security to the people of Afghanistan.

The UN regional office was staffed by young and devoted idealists, committed to the people of Afghanistan. (A few years later, this UN field office in Mazar-e-Shariff was attacked by insurgents and several UN workers and security personnel were killed. It could've been me.)

It was well after dark when we left the meeting. The kids were off the street, as temperatures had dipped well below freezing. But there was still some activity—shopping, people going here and there. The Blue Mosque was extravagantly decorated and lit, by Afghanistan's standards. There appeared to be some attempt to light the streets, homes, and stores, but the lighting was simple and sparse. In many structures there was no electrical light, and it was obvious from the faint glow in the homes that they were illuminated by candles. I was contemplative on the ride. It was dark and loud, so nearly impossible to carry on a conversation anyway. I was deep in thought. After we cleared the city, it was just like a ride in the country. I think it was the first time I'd been away from Kabul or a military base at night. There was plenty of time to think about this day of days, and oh, the places to which I had gone, and, again, how would I ever tell my wife about days like today?

The next week, to prove that there was still kite-flying in Afghanistan, the Dutch admiral rolled out of the compound, climbed the Bibi Mahrow hill in the city—a popular hangout for Kabul families—and mingled with kite-flying Afghans. The public affairs staff released a story about it, which the

Kabul-based Dutch media picked up, apparently. When I saw the admiral the next day, he lamented the fact that the Dutch media had hammered him for being on "vacation" in Afghanistan. The US Air Force sergeant who wrote the article didn't help the admiral by using the verb mingles in the headline of the release. But the admiral had an interesting day, just the same. He had seen newly built schools and toured a former Taliban checkpoint with an underground room an old Kabul man called a dungeon. Under the Taliban the boys flying kites would've been tortured for having fun.

I was looking ahead to my departure from Dover but looking back also. We had executed our only DT in a snowstorm deep into a late-January evening. Like the eighteen-inch snow the month before, it was a Saturday. It had snowed all day and our first expected aircraft had been diverted, but somehow the second managed to land. By evening heavy, fluffy snow had turned to a stinging blizzard stirred by biting and swirling winds. The snow swept across the runway and made shiny, white minitornadoes. I stood there waiting for the families to arrive, every piece of cold-weather gear I owned cloaked on some part of my body.

"It's like 'Ice Station Zebra' out here," I called out to one of my sergeants before the family arrived on the ramp and the event turned serious. He laughed but seemed to miss the sharpness of my humor. Later, when I threw out the 'Ice Station Zebra' line that I thought was really funny to some more of my younger colleagues, they respectfully half-laughed, but their chuckles melted into that blank stare of people trying to act amused but not sure why. *Ice Station Zebra* came out in 1968 and I saw it at the theater and liked it because even at eight or nine years old I was a big sports fan, and it was one of Jim Brown's first movies after his extraordinary but relatively short football career. I didn't even quiz them with names like Jim Brown, Rock Hudson, and Ernest Borgnine. Not a chance they'd know what I was talking about.

A large, florescent *18* blazed brightly on the digital thermometer at the base of the air traffic control tower. On the ramp, everything was still, and the night was eerily quiet—at first. So during the beginning of the dignified transfer I could hear every sound made, every word spoken on the plane, even up on the plane a hundred feet away. The stirring words of the chaplain's prayer rode on the wind to the families and my video team on the ground. We heard every command of the carry team NCOIC, but above all, we could not ignore the loud and uncontrollable wailing of a young wife who had just lost her soul mate and become a widow at age twenty. But she wasn't the youngest widow on the ramp that week. For a few days, that distinction belonged to the nineteen-year-old from upstate New York, whose husband's body had arrived just three nights earlier. The following Tuesday, the eighteen-year-old widow—she had graduated from high school nine months earlier—arrived to see her husband's body removed from a contract air carrier and then transported in the dead of night to the Dover Port Mortuary. The next day when I did an internet search for the media reports of the marine's death—like I did very often—I found a photograph by an embedded journalist of him on patrol in Afghanistan two months earlier. He looked happy, like he was just doing what he was meant to do. There he was, on patrol with his buddies for a cause they probably only half-understood.

The following morning we were back on the ramp at seven o'clock. This time the temperature was fifteen degrees, and the wind chill threatened the zero-degree threshold. The wind cut right through my five layers of clothes, but the real cold was the feeling on the inside, and the memories bore into my mind, and the sounds of inconsolable young women, sisters and young wives, and always mothers grieving for their sons. The following week we got our second record-breaking snowstorm—this time more than the eighteen inches of mid-December. We'd had three snowstorms during the winter and the cumulative total was more than forty inches. I took photos of my South Carolina Toyota Camry buried in snow, and drifts outside the door to our building that reached more than six feet.

We saw many fallen service members come home to Dover, and we saw dozens leave for their final resting place. The departure ceremonies normally did not include families, so there were no teenage widows, grieving mothers, or inconsolable sisters staring at the carrying case containing their baby brothers. But when the body of a popular marine from New Jersey—a former police officer whose brothers were New York City firefighters—pulled away from the front of our center, his family was there, loaded into two vans and hidden behind dark tinted windows. A squad of marines stood beside our formation, and when the chief master sergeant called us to attention and ordered us to "present arms," the hearse rolled past us, behind twenty motorcycles from the Patriot Guard Riders, a dozen police and fire department vehicles from the New York, Delaware, and New Jersey state troopers, all forming a convoy that would stretch for miles across highways between Dover and New Jersey.

At Dover, it wasn't my job to know, but I sometimes came to know the circumstances surrounding the deaths of those men and women we took care of. Several times I wandered to the secure *back of the house*, only minutes after the DT, and observed the transfer cases carefully extracted from the vans and steadied onto the conveyor belt that moved them to the mortuary. Once or twice while engaging a team member in the back, on what I thought then was a time-sensitive official matter, I exposed myself to the battered bodies just as they had been removed from the battlefield, who just a day or two earlier had been vibrant, cocky US Marines or US Army soldiers. They had died in so many ways—roadside bombs, suicide bombs, small arms fire. Then there were the vehicle rollovers, drownings, the perplexing times when their Afghan interpreters or "partners" had shot them in the back, and the unexplained, troubling suicides. There had been so many suicides, especially during the Christmas holiday season. On a few occasions I even saw the bullet holes in the heads of service members who had killed themselves with their service-issued weapons, the obvious entry and exit wounds obscured but not hidden by heavy coats of makeup.

The more DTs I witnessed, the more I thought about the war in Afghanistan. Would I ever go there again? Could we win? Was it worth the price these families were paying? I was convinced that the United States of America was performing a noble mission in Afghanistan, and I hoped that years in the future, the sacrifices of these fallen warriors, and the sacrifices of these families would make the world a better place. I thought about wars like Vietnam, where 57,000 Americans had died, and for what? Unlike World War II, where American troops and their allies had really, truly saved the world, Afghanistan had no clear-cut expectation or appearance of success and victory. World War II halted the spread of two evil empires—Japan and Germany. The war had stopped two invading forces, one in Europe, the other in the Pacific, and the world was a safer, stronger, and freer place because of that war. But Afghanistan was a war all to itself, and like no other.

After more than one hundred days, I had seen so much. Probably too much. More war than I would ever see as a public affairs officer in a combat zone. My mother back home thought I wouldn't be able to let go. I was pretty sure I could put these experiences away in a safe place once I returned to South Carolina. But while still at Dover, I couldn't get my mind around how many Americans had died at the hands of Afghan soldiers and police, our brothers-in-arms, our partners in taking back their country and returning it the people. One US soldier had been shot in the back by an insurgent who had infiltrated the Afghan National Army and wore the uniform of our allies. A captain and his private had been murdered by an Afghan interpreter the captain had dismissed from his duties because he suspected the interpreter of taking bribes from the Taliban for an assortment of operationally sensitive information.

Three days before my departure from Dover, the name of Lance Corporal Ryan McGower appeared on our board. I thought it might be my last dignified transfer. I hoped so. About twenty-five people gathered in the designated DT briefing room at the passenger terminal. Supporting airmen sat in the second and third rows. The Marine Corps carry team members sat in the front row, eating pizza. Captain Pete Gordon stood in front of the group, pointing at a white easel with aircraft diagrams and showing the positioning of the transfer vehicle, official party, family, and media parking areas.

"There will be full media and DoD media," he said. "They will be positioned here." He pointed to the media viewing area.

"When the media is in place, we will call for the family vehicles."

He then moved the pieces representing the family vehicle, carry team, transfer team, and official party. He briefed as he moved the pieces, demonstratively describing every movement and every responsibility of every person involved in the DT.

"Questions?"

There were none. So, we ate pizza and waited for the aircraft to arrive. Fifteen minutes later, when the giant 747 was on the ground and chocked, I walked alone across the dark parking ramp ahead of my team members, who had stayed in the warm briefing room until they saw the huge aft cargo door of the aircraft open. That was always our signal to move, but despite the austere conditions, I enjoyed being out here, fighting against the elements to do a job more important that my personal comfort would ever be. I set up the stanchions by myself, finishing just before my team arrived.

When the media were in place, I marshaled in the family bus. At least a dozen people climbed off, including six or seven family members. I could see them through the side windows of the bus. As the carry team and official party approached, I came to parade rest. Halfway through the DT, I came to attention and held that formation until the end. At least I thought it was the end. But something strange happened. After the dignified transfer was over, the family members lingered, reluctant to leave the ramp. So I asked the media members to get back in their van. I wanted to send it off the tarmac ahead of the family bus but was afraid that I couldn't get the media van off the ramp ahead of the family bus, which would break protocol. So, I signaled for Captain Needham to hold the van in place.

The transfer vehicle carrying the body of Lance Corporal Ryan McGower moved slowly away, and eventually far into the distance, until the red lights behind the flashing blue lights of the security forces escort vehicle had nearly disappeared through the emerging fog. But still the family members stood on the freezing ramp, and most directed their stare in the direction of the transfer vehicle. I moved carefully back in front of the bus and faced it. Finally, the funeral directors and chaplains managed to coax the family members back onto the bus. It rocked gently as they walked down the center aisle and began to retake their seats.

The family had been quiet throughout the transfer, a solemn, hushed dignity resting over the entire ramp area. But then I heard the first audible emotion, a young woman who sounded like she could not catch her breath. Then it sounded like she was choking on something, and the sound finally elevated to sobbing. Five family members were on the bus, then some of the chaplain assistants and military escorts. The sister of Ryan McGower could not be consoled. Her cries came from deep in the diaphragm, a guttural moan that took some effort to unleash, the same effort it must've required to hold all that back during the ceremony. She had stood aloof at the family center, distant and indifferent. The chaplain told me later that on the bus ride to the ramp she had been stoic. Now she was anything but stoic. She was inconsolable.

There could be no doubt that this young woman had never loved anyone like she loved that young marine, whose shattered body had come home in a flag-draped metal box. The metal box had been carefully placed into a plain white vehicle and driven slowly into the dark night. Now only distant lights could be seen. The blue flashing light of the security forces escort vehicle had made the final curve at the end of the ramp and disappeared. The red taillights from the transfer vehicle would be gone in seconds. But her sobbing grew louder and more heart-wrenching, unbridled in every way. Everyone was on the bus except the young woman and the mother—who stood motionless close to the young woman, the funeral director, and a chaplain. No one blocked her view down the ramp, even though the transfer vehicle was gone. Everyone waited patiently.

Finally, I allowed myself a quick sideways glance at the sister—the best friend and childhood protector of Ryan McGower—who had pushed away anyone who tried to comfort her, anyone who tried to convince her it would be okay, anyone who tried to usher her onto the bus. Then the mother moved closer to her again and embraced the young woman. I took a step or two to my right in anticipation of a resolution to this standoff and readied myself to marshal the bus clear of the airplane's wingtips and off the ramp. It was so quiet now. I heard the mother speak.

"Sweetheart, it's time to go," the mother said. She nudged her daughter gently. "It's time to go, honey."

"No. I'm not ready."

"Okay. We can wait a second."

The mother embraced her daughter again. She whispered in the young woman's ear. That I could not hear. They whispered back and forth as we waited. Then the girl grew louder again.

"No, Mom," she said. "That's not an answer. He had to die for something."

"He died for his country, sweetie. Now please, get on the bus."

The girl held her ground. The chaplain and funeral director stayed back, gave them space.

"I'll get on the bus when someone tells me what he died for."

Then she screamed, "What did he die for? Can someone tell me?"

The patient mother stayed remarkably calm. Everyone did. We had seen every possible reaction on this ramp. I was moved, but not surprised. The mother whispered in the daughter's ear for a long time. Finally the young woman pulled away and meandered aimlessly toward the bus. The mother followed, and then the chaplain and funeral director cued up behind the two women. The daughter stepped onto the bus, but the mother walked past the door and straight toward me. I braced for something. Something I had certainly not prepared for. We had seen every reaction, and yet this had never actually happened, not exactly in this way. I had no idea what would happen next. The heartbroken mother stood directly in front of me, her face uncomfortably close to mine.

Amazingly, I spoke first. "I'm sorry."

"Thank you for the respect you and the others have shown my family," she said.

"Yes—"

"And especially for the way you have honored my son."

"It's our privilege and duty, ma'am," I replied, surprised to have come up with an eloquent and appropriate response under such intense circumstances. "Is that your daughter?"

"It is. They were twins. Best friends. Inseparable."

This caught me off guard. "I understand," I said clumsily, although I really didn't understand. Luckily for me, she didn't call me out for the awkward reply.

"Can you tell me why my son died?" She didn't wait for an answer. "What's so important about this godforsaken place—Afghanistan—that my son had to die there?"

"I wish I had a quick and simple answer for you, ma'am," I said.

"The only way I could get her onto that damn bus was to promise my daughter I would get an answer to her question. I keep promises to my children."

"Yes ma'am."

"What do I tell her?" she asked again.

"I don't know," I said, but thinking that I should have some kind of answer. I had spent almost seven months there, but the truth is, if I asked myself the same question, I'm not sure I could come up with an adequate answer, even given time to consider a response. I had no answers.

Then she stepped forward and hugged me. It was awkward at first. I didn't know what to do, so I just hugged her back, very carefully. I looked at the chaplain and the mortuary officer, who stood close to us with blank looks on their faces.

"Maybe our paths will cross again someday," she said.

"Maybe."

She broke her embrace and turned abruptly from me. I went back to attention as she stepped onto the bus. I looked at the bus driver, who waited for me to do something, but I forgot what my next simple tasking was. So, he started forward without waiting for my signal. The bus eased off the ramp, but I stood there at attention for a long time. Captain Needham and the media members broke ranks and poured out of the van and gathered around me, even the Associated Press photographer, who, amazingly, did not ask about my brief meeting with the dead marine's mother. Perhaps he was also too stunned.

"I did *not* see that coming," Captain Needham said.

"Yeah, that's never happened before. At least not to me." I took a moment to regain my composure, then let out a subdued laugh. "Can you imagine the seizure the colonel would've had if he'd seen her hug me on the ramp?"

"I'm sure someone will brief him," Deguire said.

"Oh well, what's he gonna do, fire me?"

"He's a big enough asshole that he might just."

"Let's load up," I said.

"That's an image I wish I'd gotten," said the AP photographer.

"Yeah, I bet. Unfortunately, the family is off limits." Then I had to smile, and add, "even if they do try to gift-wrap a Pulitzer Prize for you."

Back at the office, we closed up shop quickly and I sent everyone back to their rooms, then remained behind in the office. I spent the next hour getting to know Ryan McGower, star of the football, basketball, and baseball teams, everyone's best friend, the kind of kid who was friends with the head cheerleader and the nerd at the same time. He sounded like Zach Groberg's twin. His high school principal was quoted as saying, "He made friends with the popular kids, the star athletes, and the geeks. He protected the kids who were bullied and helped little old ladies cross the street. He was an Eagle Scout and acted like one." Ryan McGower was the best our nation had to offer, and now he was gone. No wonder his sister had refused to let him go without some answers.

I sat alone in my cubicle. I had released my team members a few minutes earlier. The base photographer, who had been on the ramp with me for the Ryan McGower dignified transfer, appeared at my doorway with a thumb drive cupped in his palm. He opened his hand and let the drive roll onto his fingers.

"I have a few shots for you," he said. "Just for you, sir. Keep them close hold, please." He handed me the thumb drive.

"It's clean except for a few shots. Please wipe it clean after you download them."

"Sure," I said, puzzled.

The photographer left as abruptly as he had stealthily appeared, and I inserted the drive into my computer. I downloaded three photo files and then opened the first one. It was a tight shot of me embracing Laura McGower, the mother of Lance Corporal Ryan McGower. Now I knew her name because I had studied the DT planning sheet just minutes earlier. There was another picture of her looking straight at me with those impossible-to-answer questions in her eyes. I stared at the photos for a long time, then burned them to a compact disc and dropped it into my backpack for safe keeping.

Back at my room, I counted the number of DTs I had done. Ryan McGower was number ninety-eight. That didn't seem nearly as horrible as if the number had been one hundred.

CHAPTER THREE

MY LAST SCHEDULED dignified transfer at Dover was on a brutally cold and windy Saturday afternoon. The colonel directing the DT had to reach up several times to pull her hat tighter on her head to keep it from flying off and tumbling uncontrolled down the tarmac. The young fallen soldier had died in Iraq when his vehicle rolled over and crushed him in the forward gun hatch. The soldier's stunned, unprepared teenaged wife had authorized full media coverage when first asked by the notification officer two days earlier and a few hours after she had been told about her husband's violent and agonizing death. But when she arrived at Dover and had the procedure explained to her, she panicked, imagining photos of her husband and his crushed body ending up on Facebook, and demanded that media not be on the ramp. Steven Rook, the AP photographer who had attended and covered more dignified transfers than anyone on earth—military or civilian—and whom I had grown quite fond of during the past four months of working these cold and emotional days and nights on the Dover AFB tarmac, had already driven in from Baltimore and was sitting in the media van near the flightline entry control point.

I called Needham and told him to drive to the edge of the ramp and I would meet the vehicle there. I walked the one hundred yards or so to meet the van and had to tell Steven that the young widow had changed her mind. Better than any other media representative, he understood this completely and was gracious. I had actually taken him onto a plane for a dignified transfer and let him sit in on a DT prebrief when I misinterpreted the colonel's confusing instructions about being more open with the media and allowing them more access if they could be trusted. Steven could certainly be trusted, but when the colonel walked into a DT prebrief and saw Steven sitting stoically in the back of the room, he seethed, and later threatened to fire me although I was only following his instructions, or so I thought.

His instructions and moods fluctuated like wind. It's not surprising that several months later, after I was comfortably back at my home base in South Carolina and preparing for my second Afghanistan deployment, the colonel, who had been on fast-track to general, was demoted and humiliated for suspending civilian workers who had dared to question him on certain procedures in the back of the house—namely whether or not to trim off the protruding bone of a dead marine so his arm would fit into his uniform. It's not that this was so bad. Where the colonel erred badly in judgment was to order a civilian mortuary worker to perform the gruesome task. When the mortuary worker refused, the colonel did unceremoniously terminate him and he became the whistleblower that derailed the follow-on assignment which would've led to his promotion to general, but rather the colonel was relegated to a Pentagon desk job and fast-tracked to a premature retirement. The colonel had also made the mistake of believing the decision to trim the arm bone of the dead marine was his to make, and that the family didn't need to know. He had not bothered to ask his public affairs officer for guidance but had sent me out of the room when discussing the decision with his permanent-party staff. When I learned this whole ugly story later, I thought to myself—and perhaps mumbled aloud—that the arrogant son-of-a-bitch had actually gotten what he deserved, not for trying to do what he thought was in keeping with the family's instructions but for blaming and scapegoating subordinates when the cover-up blew up in his face. It was the worst kind of leadership that always seemed to start with one's own debilitating vanity.

So on this day, at the entry control point, moments before my last dignified transfer, Steven Rook was gracious, and I told him goodbye for today and goodbye forever. We would not see each other again.

On the ramp the widow buried her face in her hands and shook as the forty-miles-per-hour wind gusts slammed against her back and rocked her. During the DT, I looked through the clear driver's-side window and saw her through the open door. She was so young. They were all so young. When the DT was over, so was my deployment to Dover Air Force Base. Later that day, an Air Force general touring the mortuary asked me how my deployment was going.

"Going, going, gone, sir," I said, and then wished I hadn't been so casual. But since he had been the Air Force public affairs director, I hoped he wouldn't mistake my informality for disrespect.

"You're a reservist?" he asked.

"South Carolina Air National Guard, sir."

"The Swamp Foxes."

"Yes, sir."

"Well, thank you for serving here. I know it's a tough assignment."

"It was tough, sir," I said, "but important. I'll never forget this one."

I returned to my room to finish packing, and after a restless night, I set out the next morning—a cloudy Sunday—on the 600-mile drive home. I didn't cross back through Delaware and Maryland to pick up Interstate 95 near Washington, but took the scenic route, sharp and straight south through flat Delaware, then a piece of Maryland and Virginia—the Delmarva Peninsula—and reached the Chesapeake Bay at midday. I drove under the Bay and ended up in Virginia Beach. The excursion over, I worked my way to the interstate in southern Virginia, now anxious to get home. Once on the interstate the scenery became considerably less interesting, and I started to think back on the previous four months. There were so many memories packed into such little time.

But my mind was mostly occupied by the last few days, not the past four months. I couldn't get Laura McGower off my mind. I wanted to find her an answer. But I had no way of knowing that night—standing on the tarmac with her—that I would be going back someday, perhaps because I hadn't found the answers to her questions, or my own, the first time around. I had seen as much war at Dover as I had during six months in Afghanistan, when I saw parts of the four major regions of Afghanistan—Kabul, Mazar-e-Shariff, Kandahar and Herat. I had seen more of Afghanistan than most people, but much less than most also. I had not seen the enemy, not face-to-face anyway. So at the end of the long, Sunday drive, I thought back to another long trip home—back to May of 2009 and my first trip home, a time when I thought the six days in May—from the day I left Kabul until my plane touched down in South Carolina—would be the end of my Afghanistan experience.

Bagram Airfield, Afghanistan, May 9, 2009

This is the first time I can actually write about my deployment in the past tense. My deployment really ended this morning when I left HQ ISAF and flew to Bagram. It was actually difficult to leave the headquarters and Kabul. Despite my very early misgivings about having volunteered for this deployment, and the months of anxiety about being away from home, I grew attached to ISAF and even Kabul in a strange way, even though I only really experienced Kabul to a very small degree. And yet, it eventually felt like home in some way.

My last few days were memorable. My colleagues threw me a nice farewell dinner. The famous German author and journalist Christoph Reuter came to headquarters, and we drank coffee (hot chocolate) and talked. We had forged a strange friendship. My colleague Monika Winters and I sat in Destille Garden on my last night and also drank hot chocolate and talked about Afghanistan. We took one final lap around the camp and ended up at the bottom of the stairs that led to her second-story unit. Then I kissed her, once, and not long and deep, just a short, gentle kiss, halfway on the lips and halfway on the cheek. I think it was supposed to be on the cheek, but one or both of us cheated at the last possible moment.

"I've wondered for six months what that would be like." I stole that line from the movie Hoosiers when Gene Hackman finally got around to kissing Barbara Hershey.

The morning when I left my awesome German roommate Mathias was very emotional. I felt bad for leaving him behind because my departure was difficult for him. He hated Afghanistan, or the place his sister referred to in her emails—in perfect English—"fucking Afghanistan." We were talking and saying goodbye and his eyes got watery, and his voice was cracking. I think his one fear was that now he'd get a bad roommate because I tried to be a good roommate and friend. I'm not sure if he was sadder that I was leaving or sadder because he was staying. A little of both, I suppose. We were not just roommates but became good friends. Of all the people I worked with and met, he's the one person I expect to stay in contact with. (Interesting enough, I stayed in contact with dozens of people on Facebook, but immediately lost contact with my dear German friend.)

In those early and difficult days and weeks, I never expected to feel the way I did now, sentimental and almost "at home." As I meandered around the camp, thought about the first time in the Yellow Building, that Thanksgiving dinner five months earlier, the first time I had stood in these dusty intersections or sat in Destille Garden, when things that now felt so familiar and comfortable seemed so strange, I knew I would miss this place, this camp. I would miss the Afghan men who took care of my laundry, who cleaned our bathroom, and checked our meal cards at the DFAC. I didn't get to say goodbye to Colonel Murad, Baryalai Helali, and those other Afghan officials I'd worked with, some of whom reminded me of Afghan versions of American or European celebrities, like Al Pacino and The Monkees singer Davy Jones. I didn't get to say goodbye to Chris Sargent because he was in Farah on the team we sent to investigate the huge civilian casualty allegation after a big special ops mission a few nights earlier.

I spent two days at Bagram with one mission—to get myself home. I hung out at the Pat Tillman USO, took a few pictures in front of it. Interesting enough, the Polish soldiers again claimed all the seats on the US Air Force C-17s headed to Manas, so I used the National Guard connection and hopped a flight with a Kentucky Air National Guard C-130 aircrew.

For three days at Manas I began to look back on the previous six months. I decompressed there, still in a daze, sometimes wondering if it was real or had been a dream. I watched on Armed Forces Network that General McKiernan had been replaced and General McChrystal was taking his place in Afghanistan.

So, that's what I had thought, in May of 2009. And then . . .

A few weeks after I got home from Afghanistan the first time, a suicide bomber broke through the perimeter security of the Green Zone and blew himself and his vehicle up fifty meters from the main gate of HQ ISAF, where I had stood a dozen times waiting for media to show up. My friends and colleagues who were still there told me about it in emails. Jim Sinclair's training kicked in immediately. First, he dove under his desk. When he realized he was not wounded, he started to account for the people he supervised and those he worked with every day from a half dozen other nations. The bomb had shaved off the second and third floors of the building that housed many of the American female service members. It destroyed the container once occupied by my

Canadian friend John Coppard. Had he been in his hooch that day, he would've likely been killed, but he was not there. Only days earlier, he had flown to Belgium hoping doctors could diagnose the mysterious illness that had incapacitated him for long stretches of the past few months. It was a brain tumor, and a few years after he survived the suicide bombing, the brain tumor killed him.

I didn't need to be reminded—but Jim reminded me several times—how often I had stood outside the main gate to meet journalists and escort them onto the compound. He reminded me of the time when I had returned from church one Friday and stood outside the gate and emptied my pockets, giving the Afghan kids every piece of candy, my Slim Jims, and the coins in my pocket. Then I came into the compound, got more candy, and returned to the group of kids, which had grown into a mob. Then I paid an ice cream vendor $20 to empty his cart. The kids keep coming. Soon, I was surrounded, and my situation became precarious because there were more kids and not enough candy and ice cream to go around. The Afghan security guards outside the gate jumped into the fray, scattered the kids, and freed me.

So, when I sat at home in late May and read about the suicide bombing outside the HQ ISAF gate, I couldn't help but imagine what would've happened if the vehicle-borne suicide bomb had appeared at the same time as that mob of children had gathered. I probably would've been killed along with many of those children, and I would've been in the international news for all the wrong reasons.

After returning from Dover, I felt lost and alone. I went through the motions for a few years, built the lake house, and then got serious about planning for retirement. But I wasn't ready for it when the wing commander handed me my six-month letter. My last day in the Guard was going to be December 31, 2012. Then, a second Afghanistan deployment was offered, and I went around the chain of command—which my commanders never forgot—and straight to the general to request a six-month extension so I could deploy again. Why?

Why not? My wife had decided to work for a few more years as a nurse, and then retire. I had caught all the fish I could stand to clean. My children were grown and away, either with their spouses or college roommates. Doing public affairs for the military at home when the war in Afghanistan waged on just didn't make any sense to me. Then three South Carolina National Guard soldiers were killed by a suicide bomber in Afghanistan and my work at home seemed temporarily important again. When their bodies were en route to Dover, my leadership asked me what it was like at Dover, to describe the procedures at the mortuary. When the remains returned to the local airport—and at the funeral—I was there. People kept thanking *me* for my service. I recalled why I had volunteered for Afghanistan the first time—because people kept thanking me for my service. But at that time I had only served at home, wrapped in safety and security, going home to my family every night after work. The thought of going back to Afghanistan—something I swore I would never do—took me back to that first mind-numbing journey—when I first set foot on brown, dusty Afghan soil.

In the skies above Afghanistan—October 30, 2008

On the flight from Manas Air Base, Kyrgyzstan to Afghanistan, the United States Air Force C-17 was packed with men of the Polish land forces. I had not even seen them back at Manas—on the base, in the dining hall, or at the gym. Or perhaps I had seen them but didn't know it. I had not been told many things in advance of my Afghanistan deployment. No one had advised me to study and memorize the flags of NATO and non-NATO nations—excluding the

American, British, Australian, Canadian, German, and other familiar flags—because it would be the primary method of differentiating a Polish soldier from a Hungarian air force lieutenant colonel in the melting pot of nations fighting side by side in the common cause of Afghanistan. Certainly I had never expected to serve alongside the Polish. But in the Manas passenger terminal, I sought out the commanding officer and English speaker, and had learned more of Poland in that one hour than at any time in my life prior to that. The Polish defied all the stereotypes I had heard as a kid. They were strong and absolutely sure of themselves. And they were smart—smart enough to take the good seats, the airline seats, referred to as the "comfort pallet." I was one of the highest-ranking officers on the plane but had to squeeze into a web seat on the side of huge plane's inner belly.

The flight was short and smooth, the packed cargo compartment of the enormous C-17 dark and warm. The noise of the engines drowned out any attempt at conversation. Every man and woman on the aircraft rode alone with their thoughts. I was deep inside my own thoughts, where there was enormous silence drowned out by the noise of the airplane.

I was encumbered by body armor and pinned to my seat by the heavy backpack in my lap and computer case I straddled between my feet. I wanted to get up and look out the small, circular window, curious to examine the mysterious terrain below, though nighttime lingered. In the window across the belly of the airplane from me I could see the faint light of day breaking. Of all the many things I might have thought about, questions to be pondered, experiences to be anticipated and played out in advance, I thought of Vietnam. It was the war of my youth, fought in a far away land and always in competition with the highlighted experiences of my formative years. The Vietnam War had passed through my childhood on a parallel timeline with elementary school, Little League baseball, moving from the city to the country when I was twelve, junior varsity football, my first date—not the real kind, with just me and a girl, in my car. But the kind of date for which parents provided the transportation. I had been much too busy with adolescence and high school football to give much thought to the war's violent and traumatic conclusion and couldn't be bothered as to whether the war had been won or lost until studying it as a military officer years later. Still, I only knew about Vietnam from flicks like Platoon and Forrest Gump—and news footage, and force-reading those thick and exhaustive historical journals and analyses by the so-called experts. I had seen The Killing Fields and Apocalypse Now and had read Going After Cacciato in college but didn't remember them well. In the next hour I would know more about Afghanistan than I would ever know about Vietnam. We landed as morning broke.

On the ground at Bagram Air Field, where my feet first touched Afghan soil, those odd movie clips from Platoon and Forrest Gump played weirdly in my mind—Charlie Sheen egressing the helicopter, trying to protect his eyes from the swirl of dust churned up by the chopper's main rotor blade, Forrest and Bubba awkwardly crawling from their helicopter then jumping back to dodge their duffel bags, which were tossed unceremoniously from the helo, landing at their feet. Like Charlie, Forrest, and Bubba, I too felt lost and clueless, as green as the day I'd entered the Air Force officer training school, despite having twenty-three years of service behind me and silver oak leaves on my collar. Then the movie clips faded, and I stood on the edge of a hot tarmac, my excessive six bags contributing to a large palletized load of duffel bags and suitcases. The pallet was carried away and I climbed onto a crowded bus.

The Poles vanished, rushed away on different buses. Six months later, on my way out of Afghanistan, I'd have to compete against them again for seats on American C-17s.

Bagram. Total chaos. Chaos with a purpose, I hoped and assumed, a method to the madness I did not yet comprehend. The tarmac was crowded with aircraft of every kind, constantly coming and going, the many sounds of engines and rotor blades, generators, and ground vehicles creating an ensemble of persistent noise that came at me from all directions. The area around the aircraft parking ramp was equally active, bordered by endless stacks of containers, an assortment of vehicles static and in motion. Behind all that were rows of tents and thrown together prefabricated buildings. The narrow, congested roads were squeezed by the containers and tents and buildings and clogged by the collection of vehicles and people on foot, all trying to get somewhere in a hurry, but unable to.

The next movie clips that played in my head were my own. I had been on the ground in Afghanistan less than thirty minutes and already had a surreal feeling that this was someone else's story, that I was watching another one of those war movies—a film about someone arriving in Afghanistan green as the first day he ever put on the uniform, anxious and yet certain he was supposed to be here. Afghanistan had been on my mind for months. I had thought for many years that someday I'd come here, although the final commitment to volunteer had come recently and spontaneously. My connection to Afghanistan was not completely new.

For no good reason at all I didn't like Bagram. I suppose only because it was the last intermediate stop between the home I'd left behind and my new home, the NATO Headquarters of the International Security Assistance Force, my assigned duty for the next six months. My goal had not been to reach Afghanistan, but to complete the task and leave the combat zone knowing my mission was complete. It was something I needed to check off my list of accomplishments before wrapping up my military career. On this day, that journey had begun.

I wandered between several rows of Quonset huts and tents, looking for the building where the ammo was. When I finally found it, a private issued me two clips of M-9 ammunition and sent me on my way.

At the helicopter terminal I was told to wait, but within ten minutes, three or four soldiers began grabbing my gear and dragging it toward the helicopter ramp. I followed them to an idling UH-60 Blackhawk.

"Climb in, sir," the crew chief yelled above the noise of the rotor blades.

"What about the others?" I asked, referring to a handful of airmen who had been sitting on their bags near the helicopter long before I arrived.

"They are already booked on another flight," the sergeant yelled. "This is your flight!"

I did as I was told. If it had been my mission to keep the Bagram stopover short, then mission accomplished. My time at Bagram was so frantic and disorderly that I boarded the Blackhawk without retrieving my M-9 pistol from the locked case. I pushed into my seat and strapped in across from two mysterious civilians—contractors, private security consultants, CIA operatives, special forces. I had no idea who I was sharing the Blackhawk with. So, as we taxied away from the aircraft parking ramp, I sat strapped into my seat, first time in a combat zone, with two mysterious civilians sitting across from me—locked and loaded—and my weapon still packed in the secure carrying case. I had been awake for eighteen hours. I was hot and hungry, exhausted from hauling around six bags in full body armor. Fear surged through me for the first of many times. I didn't know enough to be afraid that insurgents might be waiting in the hills for a chance to ambush the low-flying, slow-flying Blackhawk. What I feared was the sudden churning in my stomach and the emerging and nasty, salty thirst that preceded vomit. That taste worked its way into the back of my throat, and I mouthed the first of what would be many silent prayers. Please God, don't let me throw up. I didn't want the humiliation of barfing, but even worse, I just didn't have anything to vomit into, except maybe my helmet. I knew a rocket attack against our Blackhawk would've been worse, but at that moment I wasn't sure anything could be worse than throwing up all over the floor of the Blackhawk, or into my helmet, or all over the mysterious civilians.

Once airborne, my stomach settled, and the salty taste subsided. From my window seat in the Blackhawk, I saw Afghanistan for the first time, a dull, rippled expanse of light brown. The valleys were flat and brown, with a rare green streak that gave away desperately flowing water. The hills rose brown and rocky. Afghanistan rolled up underneath me like an endless dusty brown blanket. In other words, there were no words to quite describe my very impressions. In the far distance I got my very first glimpse of the higher mountains I'd seen in photos. Over the next six months, I would rarely go anywhere in Afghanistan where I couldn't see those mountains.

We flew over villages of square, walled compounds, each compound housing a large and extended family—I supposed—the patriarch and his wife (or wives), parents, children, brothers, and their wives. Would there be sisters, or would they have been married off to another family and live in a separate compound somewhere? I actually saw children running around in the "yards" below. What must life be like down there? I thought.

The Blackhawk navigated between some small mountains and then made a complete circle north of Kabul in preparation for touchdown at Kabul International Airport. It was during this banked circle that I first saw two other Blackhawks in the formation, all three trailed by an AH-64 Apache attack helicopter, the armed escort that had protected our flight from Bagram to Kabul.

On the tarmac at Kabul International Airport, my half dozen bags were tossed unceremoniously onto the tarmac—just like Forrest and Bubba's duffel bags—dragged fifty feet from the helicopter and stacked clear of the turbulence created by rotor blades still turning overhead. I stood by my bags, stared back at the helicopter, then toward the perimeter of the tarmac. There was only one way for me to go. The mystery civilians stayed on the Blackhawk, and it flew away. I moved my bags, two at a time, to the edge of the ramp and thought again of Charlie Sheen in Platoon during those first moments after his arrival in Vietnam, blinded by the dust from the rotor blades, lost from the very first moment he had arrived in the strange, exotic, and war-ravaged land, stunned that he had actually dropped out of college to volunteer. I had left the comforts of home to volunteer. Now I asked myself the same question.

Why had I left behind my safe and comfortable life to come so far away from home and family to this strange and battered land, buried in hopelessness? Why would any clear-thinking person do this?

Kabul International Airport is known by the letters KAIA rather than the standard three-letter designation, avoiding the ominous KIA. No one would want to land a plane in a combat zone at an airport designated KIA. Soldiers from at least a dozen nationalities loitered outside the terminal.

Everyone was armed up, geared up, and looked like they knew what they were doing. I had still not yet pulled my weapon from the case. This was the last leg of my confirmed transportation. From here I was on my own. I thought no one from HQ ISAF knew I was coming at this time, on this day, and so no one rolled up in front of the restaurant called Air Force One to load up my bags and drive me to the compound. But it was still early in the day, so I took my first breather in the past twelve hours, finally pulled my M-9 from the locked case, strapped it to my body armor and slid a magazine into the ammo belt also attached to my body armor. Now I didn't feel quite so awkward.

Finally, I took a deep breath, then my first long and detailed look at KAIA. Vietnam, I thought. I would make a half dozen trips back to KAIA in my first five weeks in Kabul, but it would never look or feel the same as this first time, a strange and chaotic place that scared me on my first day there. Later, I would get comfortable here, deliver and pick up soldiers, board planes, await the arrival of dignitaries, collect a German navy captain, and deliver him to Mazar-e-Sharif, pose for photos with attractive female Belgian officers, escort greenies around this place, and unintentionally make them look naive and foolish, just the way I felt today. All that would happen in a matter of weeks.

Sergeant Shelly Smith snatched me from this deep and silent observation of my surroundings.

"You're Lieutenant Colonel Watson? We were told you were coming," she said exuberantly.

Thank God, I thought. Someone knows I'm alive and in country.

"Did we know you were coming today? Are you booked on Movecon?" Was I booked on Movecon? Had I ever heard of Movecon, the heavily armed convoy run by the British that shuttled NATO soldiers to various locations in the Kabul area?

"I wasn't able to get word to the camp that I was coming on this flight," I said. "I got out of Bagram faster than expected."

I knew instantly I was in good hands, figuratively scooped up by a female Air Force sergeant, attractive in a rugged and assertive sort of way. Her uniform was dulled by the prevalent Afghan dust. She wore a helmet and body armor, an M-16 strapped across her chest. She carried a backpack that looked like it must've weighed five hundred pounds, bulging with the gear of a combat photographer— camera, tripod, batteries, and other accessories tied to it by various means. She smiled, lit a cigarette, and waited for the Movecon vehicles to approach, as sure of herself as any person could be.

Five minutes later, two hideous, customized armored vehicles rolled to a stop in front of Air Force One. Duffel bags and backpacks were stacked high on the roof of the vehicles, secured by web material. British commandos jumped from the vehicles, opened the back doors, and four or five soldiers of various nationalities piled from the back of each. One commando climbed atop each vehicle, loosened the webbing, and lowered the bags to awaiting arms below.

The convoy commander—a corporal—stepped into a circle of soldiers.

"If you have a seat reserved for this shuttle, please step forward and tell me your name," he said with a sharp British accent. When he had checked off the names, Sergeant Smith stepped in.

"Corporal, this is our new public affairs officer. He needs a ride to HQ."

"We have a full load, sir," he said directly to me, "but one no-show right now . . ." He looked closely at his list. "Major

Haney. If he doesn't show, you can have his seat, no worries, sir."

"He's not going to be here," I said. "He was still waiting on the ramp at Bagram when I left. I know he's not here."

"Good enough then," the corporal said. "Let's get you loaded up, sir."

He grabbed the first of my bags and tossed it to the soldier atop one of the vehicles. Sergeant Smith and I handed the other bags up, and I thought maybe the tires on the vehicle sank just a little.

"Gather 'round," the corporal said. "Listen up, please. I'm Corporal Walker. I'll be your convoy commander for this trip."

The convoy briefing was just another reality check. Walker pulled out a pair of toy cars and placed them strategically on the hood of his lead vehicle. He started by describing the damage inflicted by an improvised explosive device that had been detonated on the streets of Kabul earlier in the day. He reminded us of the massive and deadly suicide bombing in front of the Indian Embassy just a few weeks before. I thought a few times, Did he really say that? He turned one of the toy cars on its side. "If the lead vehicle is hit," he said, then explained to us how we would egress the disabled vehicle and take cover in the back vehicle and fight our way out of danger until we could take refuge at a NATO base.

Finally I knew it was time to dispense with all the "we aren't in Kansas anymore" clichés. I was in the combat zone, and I knew it when we packed into the back of the convoy vehicles, locked and loaded our weapons, and designated a gunner at the rear door—one of the enlisted troops with a loaded and charged M-16. I closed my eyes, felt closed in on all sides, claustrophobic and nervous. The vehicle bounced away from the KAIA parking area through the checkpoints and onto the dirty and bumpy streets of Kabul.

I twisted slightly to look out the small side window. Then I leaned forward to see out the dirty back windows. I could not see much, but what I saw on that first drive was very truly indescribable. What I saw—or what I thought I saw—was an endless ghetto in the capital city of a country torn apart by war. I would never forget that first drive through a portion of Kabul, but each time I drove these streets after the first day, Kabul would somehow look and feel a little bit different and familiar. In time I would develop a peculiar and emotional attachment to the city, and even to these people that I would never know. On the first day, I did not consider walking on the streets, but later I would begin to wish I could get out, walk the streets freely, mingle with the people. But not today. What I saw on the first day were the by-products of war— poverty and a devastated infrastructure. What I didn't see— or understand—were conditions had actually improved, and everywhere there were signs of hope and progress. But to my untrained eyes, on my first day in Kabul, I saw nothing but devastation and despair. I didn't know that we were driving through one of the poorest and most shattered sections of Kabul, close to the airport and always near the fighting, away from the city center. In the days and weeks to come, I would see better parts of Kabul.

My first impressions of the HQ ISAF compound were the same—some kind of combat zone from another war I had neither participated in nor studied closely. My first look at the compound set off a suffocating claustrophobia that I suppressed with feigned enthusiasm. I felt instantly boxed in, like a mouse in a maze, trapped in some sort of gray prison thrown together with metal boxes on a gray dirt pallet that created narrow lanes and blinding dust. Every thought from the time I had left South Carolina until the moment I arrived on the compound was about getting to Kabul and the headquarters. That single-minded quest had driven me and my mind to press forward and had mostly taken my thoughts off what and whom I had left behind. But then I finally reached the headquarters compound of the International Security Assistance Force, and it instantly hit me—I would be here for the next six months and there was nothing I could do to change that. My family was now a million miles away and my heart nearly broke in those early days. I thought I would never get home to my family. I vowed that if I ever got home to my family, I would never leave them again.

That had been my first arrival in Afghanistan. Now, after giving it very little thought, I was going back. I got better predeployment training this time, a two-week course at Fort Dix, New Jersey. Unlike my first predeployment training, where I was the only lieutenant colonel, there were a few more the second time around. Except they were in their late thirties, not in their early fifties like me. I was three months removed from knee surgery and every drill, every crawl, every dash across an open field was painful and exhausting for me.

I had my second Norway experience, on the other side of the country this time. At Stavanger, I trained with officers and NCOs from a dozen nations. We bunked on a Norwegian military training base, where hundreds of eighteen-year-olds rolled in to start their mandatory one-year military service. I wandered into the theater one evening while they were watching the American hit comedy "The Big Bang Theory." At one point a particular funny scene played out and I laughed aloud, while every kid in the theater remained stoic. Their English was excellent, but their understanding of American humor channeled through the lens of Cal Tech nerds was not, apparently. On a free Saturday, we took a circuitous route—taxi, ferry boat, and bus—to the iconic and breathtaking Preikestolen—the Pulpit Rock, where thousands of visitors had climbed to what seemed like the top of the world, and where a few couples had even pledged to each other their undying love just before stepping off the ledge and falling to their deaths into the icy waters of Lysefjord six hundred meters below. Afghanistan would follow Norway.

Manas was different the second time. Instead of sharing a small room with a "spook," I shared a giant tent with a dozen American airmen and a few hundred soldiers from Georgia (the country, not the state). On the C-17 flight from Manas to Bagram, I worked my way onto the flight deck and looked below as we crossed into Afghan air space, across majestic mountains. It felt like coming home, to some degree, but I knew it wouldn't feel that way for long. It was another one of those experiences I'd look back on with some degree of disbelief—had I really flown into Afghanistan standing in the cockpit of a C-17 and looking out the window and the breathtaking landscape below? Yes, I actually had.

At Bagram, I was impatient, so instead of waiting for a helicopter like I had on my first trip, I squeezed myself and an Air Force captain onto a rickety old commuter plane. Big mistake, I thought, once I was on board and it was too late to turn back. At Kabul International Airport, I called the PA shop, and an exuberant Army lieutenant and a stocky Marine private showed up an hour later in an armored vehicle. It was considerably smoother than my arrival four years earlier, but when you've done it all once before, you feel like an expert.

As we drove through the streets of Kabul, I remembered that first time four years ago, the briefing by the English corporal, my first view of Kabul's potholed streets, all those poor people moving about. This time I looked for signs of improvement and progress, kept thinking I saw signs of it, but maybe it was just what I wanted to see. A few minutes later, I was at HQ ISAF, a familiar drumbeat pounding in my chest. The journey had started all over again. For days, I just couldn't quite believe this either, that I had come back for a second sojourn in this war-ravaged country of Taliban extremists and peace-seeking Afghan citizens.

Interestingly enough, I again arrived in Afghanistan just days before the presidential election in America. In 2008 I had watched the Obama speech from Chicago's Grant Park in the ballroom of the Hotel Serena, where I was attending a NATO strategic communications workshop. I got caught up in the fervor of that historic event. But after four years of mediocre leadership and unfulfilled promises, I had backed Mitt Romney and was bitterly disappointed when the American people rejected the hope I had that Romney would lead us during the next four years. This time I avoided the president's speech altogether.

As if the presidential election wasn't depressing enough, I had my first office call with my new boss, Colonel Jack Daniels.

"Just answer the mail," he said. "Keep the press desk email box clear and keep the media questions answered. That's all you can do. We have no relationship with the Afghans. We're always gonna have to do everything for them. I don't think that's going to change."

It almost sounded like he was saying there was no chance of success here. I was glad Laura McGower had not heard that speech. She would have never found any answers for her daughter.

A few minutes after leaving Colonel Daniels's office, I was having trouble breathing. Panic had set in. I rushed out of the office and luckily found the chaplain, where I confided in him that I had made a huge mistake coming back here a second time. Somehow, when I left his office, I felt better.

CHAPTER FOUR

I HAD FELT good the first few days, the home sickness and separation anxiety seemingly in check. On day three, one week after I had left home, it hit me—the overwhelming anxiety and self-doubt that I recalled very well from my first experience here, the realization of what I had gotten myself into. On one side of the world—back home—I felt restless and underachieving. So, those emotions drove my decisions. On the other side of the world—in brown, air-polluted Afghanistan—I felt trapped. The classic metaphor of wanting something you can't have, or the more you can't have something, the more you want it, all of that nonsense. Everything was triggered by that disheartening meeting with Colonel Daniels. I didn't drink alcohol, so I had never had a Jack Daniels, but I knew now it was a bitter drink, for which I would have a hard time developing a taste. I'm sure he had heard a few Jack Daniels quips in his long and distinguished career, but I bet he had never heard that one.

For two days I couldn't find anything positive to motivate me. I somehow hid from my colleagues and bosses the dark depression and anxiety that nearly engulfed me. I survived on sheer determination—and desperation. I had no choice. I was here for six months, voluntarily, so I had to push through it with some kind of strength and fortitude I didn't know I had, but apparently did. Push through—a term we used to prescribe our emergency actions while in a convoy if we run into trouble. If, God forbid, we get attacked. Or, if a brazen Afghan National Police officer tries to stop us at a checkpoint, wants to press some bogus dispute about the vehicle passes in our windshield, or thinks perhaps he could snatch a little fee from us for passing by his post. We push through. The perplexing thing was, we knew 99 percent of the Afghan soldiers and police were our allies. But we had to watch out for that 1 percent who had been radicalized or threatened by the insurgency, who had become careless, unscrupulous, bribed, or worse, deadly.

"If we get in trouble, just push through, hard," I told my troops on my first convoy back to Kabul International Airport to drop off two of our colleagues who were going home.

Push through. That phrase echoed in my head day and night. It was hard—again—being away from home and adjusting to this environment. Everyone around me seemed so comfortable and well-adjusted, but were they dying inside like me? I managed to portray a strong and confident outward appearance while my heart was always churning up inside my chest. Maybe most of the other people were feeling the same way—but just coping better.

Then there was the job. Everyone around me seemed confident and sure of themselves. They seemed to understand all the issues and knew all the right people to call, all the right places to look for information, and all the right things to write or say when they responded to a media inquiry or provided some other kind of requested information. I had been here before. I remember those early days of my first deployment, how everything seemed so unfamiliar, and I seemed so unsure. After a few months, I would be the seasoned veteran and there would be other new people who would struggle the same way. I told myself to "answer the mail," as my colonel had instructed.

One of my other primary responsibilities was to advise and prep the senior ISAF spokesperson—a hotshot, fish-out-of-water German fighter pilot brigadier general named Dieter Kinkel—for interviews and media round tables. On my second or third day, we had a "coffee" in the garden (I had a hot chocolate), and he asked me about my family, let me in on some inner workings of the rocky relationship between him and my boss.

"You are a part of my team, my inner circle," the general told me.

He immediately began inviting me to sit in on interviews and included me in briefings, in the early days with colonels from the Ukraine and Croatia. We made a unique international foursome. The Ukraine colonel had started his military career in the Soviet Army. I told him I had just flown over Ukraine days earlier on my way to Afghanistan, and that my son-in-law had been a missionary there and was fluent in the language. I wanted to ask the Croatian why he was even here. Shouldn't he be back home, protecting his homeland from another ethnic cleansing by the Serbs? I had never studied the whole Yugoslavia, Serbia, Croatia, Bosnia crisis enough to really understand it, but I didn't really understand Afghanistan that well either. I'm sure the Croatian colonel would have had some stories to tell but asking him to tell them would've been a monumental breach of nation-to-nation protocol. That would be like asking General Kinkel what he thought of Hitler. I always found it interesting to serve with Germans, like my roommate Matthias from my first deployment.

I watched the generals every day, worked with them, sometimes advised them. I secretly wanted to be one of them, and thought maybe I could be, although they just seemed to have a deeper understanding, something I didn't feel like I had, or would ever obtain. I was a lieutenant colonel heading up the media ops desk. I was capable of doing that job well. But I also knew I had probably reached the limit of my capabilities and wasn't going any higher. My name would never be mentioned in any historical narrative of the Afghanistan War, as long as I stayed alive. But what I could do, and would do, was watch, learn, and listen, observe what was going on around me, and when I thought about her, find answers to Laura McGower's question, and hopefully find answers to my own questions as well. When I finished this tour, I would have spent one year of my life in this country, and I knew I would want to know what for. I had questions of my own, similar to the question Laura McGower had voiced on the ramp at Dover. My question went something like this: "Can someone tell me why I'm here? What did I spend a year of my life in Afghanistan for?"

The first week dragged along. I wanted to be busy, but it was slow—if a military campaign can be called slow. In order for me to be busy and push hard every day at a feverish pace, engage in a way that would seem to make the days go by much faster, something bizarre—probably catastrophic—would have to happen, on the battlefield, in the city, at the presidential palace. I didn't want young soldiers or Afghan civilians to die so I could be busy. I didn't want to deal with a deadly helicopter crash or suicide bomber attack so I could feel needed, just so the days on the calendar would appear to turn over faster.

Just as I thought this, we got busy on the first day of my second week, and good people did have to die. An Afghan man wearing the uniform of the Afghan National Army shot and killed a British Army captain while Afghans and Brits played football together. Not even in this bizarre country did people shoot each other over a soccer match, but apparently there was some dispute between the two. We never got a satisfactory explanation. A British guardian angel—an overlook—shot and killed the Afghan attacker just moments after he turned the weapon on the captain. The guardian angel did his job, preventing other possible deaths. But this was my first insider attack, the first of many, the kind of troubling violence I had heard so much about from home in recent months, the kind of attack that threatened to undermine the partnership between the Afghans and the coalition. It would not play well back in England, where the people were already angry, and they would more strongly demand of their government a full accounting of why British blood, the people would argue, was being so recklessly spilled on Afghan soil. There would most certainly be an investigation. But it would be difficult to learn the reasons behind the tragedy because a vigilant, or vigilante, British sharpshooter had killed the man who had killed his comrade.

Just when we thought the insurgency could no longer effectively—yes, effectively—attack us, an insurgent missile landed inside a combat outpost in eastern Afghanistan and killed an American soldier. A few days later I saw his name and photo on the Facebook page Freedom Remembered. He was young, like so many of those young kids whose fragmented bodies had arrived at Dover. Though they could occasionally kill NATO soldiers, the insurgents were more effective at attacking innocent civilians. It was not just a by-product of the insurgency, but a ruthless tactic to magnify the chaos, heighten anxiety, and undermine the Afghan government and the people's trust in the Afghan National Security Forces. The insurgents planted roadside bombs that were often run over by Afghans—like the family in Khost who were returning home from the hospital with their older children and newborn baby when their van hit a roadside bomb, killing all six members of the family, including the two-day-old baby. It was now a war on the people. Something we attacked ourselves with the information war.

Roadside bombs and the volatile issue of insider attacks, what we often referred to as "green-on-blue," didn't make me think too much about Laura McGower. But this high-visibility initiative called reintegration would certainly grab her attention if she watched the news closely and read some of the comments about it. If I ever saw her again, I wanted to be able to tell her success stories, and how this was now a better and more stable country, and that her son did not die in vain. But what would she think of reintegration—the ground-breaking Afghan-led effort to coax the insurgents out of the fight and provide them an opportunity to rejoin their families and communities? More than five thousand low- and mid-level Taliban fighters had already done this. It was viewed as a great success. How would my email to her read?

Dear Mrs. McGower,

I just wanted to inform you about this wonderful program here called Reintegration. It's been very successful. The insurgent who planted the improvised explosive device that killed your son has been pardoned and returned to his village and family. He is not only getting job training and a salary—paid for by your tax dollars—but all is forgiven, and he is once again a member of his family and community.

It seemed impossible to imagine, but officials often described the day when the war would end, and the enemy might no longer be our enemy. But, there were plenty of precedents from our nation's own history. England is our closest ally. Japan isn't far behind. A German general had invited me into his inner circle.

General Kinkel invited me into an interview with two well-read Pakistani journalists, who tried hard to engage him on the conflict of cross-border fires from Pakistan into Afghanistan. He was cordial, as always, and charmed them, but wouldn't allow himself to be pulled into operational—not strategic—discussions.

"This is the first time I engaged with Pakistani journalists," he told them. "I am grateful that you came today."

The Pakistan journalists were respectful but demanding, and seemed to push the general toward admitting that there was a chance the whole campaign could fail and the Afghan National Army would collapse without the constant support and mentorship of coalition forces. Civil war might follow, or a return to the darkness of the Taliban, who would close schools and murder girls and women who tried to go to school, or work in business and government. I didn't want to think of that worst-case scenario. In the interviews, especially this early in my tour, I usually remained silent, careful not to upstage the general. But, on this day, I spoke up, not sure if it was my place to do so. After all, he was the official spokesman.

"I think because the ANA fails sometimes that people don't want to give them any credit for success," I stated.

The general looked at me. He frowned slightly, and I thought maybe I had spoken out of turn and that perhaps a reprimand was forthcoming.

The interview ended and after I escorted the reporters back to the gate, I went straight back to the general's office to evaluate the interview. I spoke first.

"Sir, I'm sorry if I spoke out of turn, it's just—"

He interrupted my apology and I braced for a rebuke.

"No, that's absolutely fine," he countered quickly in his fluent and eloquent accented English. "He wanted us to admit there's a chance for failure and I will not go there. We are here to succeed."

"I agree. This is very personal for me, sir," I said. "When I get home, I will have spent—like you, sir—one year of my life here. I want us to succeed."

"Yes, me too. There are no other options in my mind."

"Remember I told you about my documentary project?"

He nodded and I continued.

"I've interviewed the families of many American soldiers and marines who have died in this country. And we're losing people almost every day. Too much has been lost here for me to be pessimistic. I have to maintain hope that all the sacrifices will be worth it someday. There's just too much blood on the ground."

He agreed. His eyes told me so.

It was a good discussion that I wish we could've continued, but I had a movement to Kabul International Airport to deliver two of our colleagues who had completed their deployments and were heading home. I rode in the front seat with a Marine sergeant, who wanted to own the road. It was so difficult not to order him to slow down, especially when Afghan children, oblivious to the dangers all around them, strolled around the edge of the roads with their minds apparently in so many different places. It was still their city after all. Just like my early excursions through Kabul four years ago, I would, if I could, try to come up with some words to describe what I saw. But one would just have to see them for themselves to get any kind of picture of the chaos that was the streets of Kabul.

On the day before Thanksgiving, the insurgents tried to strike close to the seat of NATO power in Kabul. And I made a name for myself. I was sitting at my desk with the window open when I heard an explosion in the distance.

"What was that?" I said, startled.

"Not sure," Henry Belgrade said, his reply not close to matching the excitement in my question.

Charlie Church got on the phone to the SAR while I stood by the window and listened to the giant voice booming over the loudspeakers around the base. I could barely make out the message.

"What are they saying?" Charlie asked.

"Stay clear of the windows," I said, chuckling, then backing away.

Then we heard *boom, boom, boom* off in the distance.

"Rockets," I said.

"Sounds like it," Henry replied calmly.

"I think the first noise was an explosion, probably an IED. But I think those are rockets impacting somewhere out there," I guessed.

The messages continued to rumble across the giant voice, a woman's voice, which perhaps was intended to defuse the tension.

"Camp Lockdown," she said.

"Let's account for our people," Henry directed.

"Where's Isabelle?" I asked.

"Already on it," Charlie said, his cell phone pushed to his ear. A moment later, I heard him say, "We're in lockdown. Just stay in your room." After a beat, he added, "We don't know yet. Maybe an IED or rockets. Henry wants everyone to stay put."

The news hit the Kabul news media fast. The local reports beat our operational reporting and were pretty accurate. A suicide bomber, perhaps two, had attempted to approach a gate of Camp Eggers or the US Embassy. High-strung members of the Afghan National Security Forces had acted quickly and decisively. When the bombers did not follow orders, the ANSF fired first, dropping the suicide bombers, one of whom managed to detonate his vest, killing two Afghan security guards and the two insurgents. An ISAF vehicle—which may or may not have been the intended target—was hit by shrapnel from the blast.

It limped back into camp, battered and bruised, but the passengers were unharmed. I meandered into the motor pool later that day curious to see what an armored vehicle looked like after surviving a suicide bomber. It was riddled with holes on the passenger side, and I was pretty sure the red, sticky matter clinging to the vehicle was bits and pieces of human flesh from the bombers. That day I was quoted for the first time as an ISAF spokesman—in the *Los Angeles Times*—telling a reporter there were no injuries to ISAF personnel and that our compounds were safe and secure. That was our story.

My fame grew astronomically later in the day, when I simply hit send on a very brief email to the media declaring that General Allen, the commander of ISAF and US Forces in Afghanistan, had returned to Kabul after being in Washington for three weeks. An Associated Press reporter stated it this way: "Lt. Col. Bristow Watson, a spokesman for the International Security Assistance Force, said General Allen returned to Kabul on Wednesday." The rest of the story recapped the general's tumultuous trip to Washington, where he had been relentlessly interrogated after being accused of sending out inappropriate emails to a female colleague, which had made him the subject of a Department of Defense inspector general investigation. The general did not want to see every media outlet in the world report that he returned to work and was still the subject of this investigation. And he was probably wondering *Who in the hell is Lt. Col. Bristow Watson?* But the story and my statement had gone viral.

Colonel Jack Daniels walked out of his office at about eight o'clock that evening with a printed email in his hand.

"Hey Brist, you got your first feedback from COMISAF."

If I was looking for some positive response to my newfound fame, it was not forthcoming. The sarcastic email simply read "Obviously, I want to call a lot of attention to this." Oops.

"You can keep that for a souvenir," Daniels said.

"Just in case this is your last day as a spokesman for ISAF," Henry Belgrade chimed in.

It was amazing that a minor player like me sometimes acted on the world's biggest stage. First, it was the General Allen quote, where I was attributed in a huge, international story. Then, when Senator Lindsey Graham—a personal friend from South Carolina—made a prediction about the future of Afghanistan and its girls and young women on Fox News, I thought maybe he was helping me find answers for Laura McGower, a woman he had never met, and whom I would not likely ever see again. He said, "When Afghanistan ends, it needs to end well. We need to bring most of our troops home. But if you left 15,000 or 20,000 behind in Afghanistan with airplanes and helicopters and special forces units, that'd be the end of the Taliban, and those young women would have a chance." Well said, Senator.

Of course, the 15,000 or 20,000 troops would be much debated over the next year, long after my Afghanistan experience was over. But, isn't that what we wanted, for the young women to have a chance? Would that give grieving mothers and heartbroken sisters an answer? Would that help Laura McGower and her daughter find some peace? Would that give them hope that their beloved Ryan had died for something?

On a Saturday night, I hiked with Charlie Church, Isabelle, and our civilian media engagement chief Missy Chabon to the American Embassy for surf-n-turf night. We made fun of the embassy employees, who lived in apartments with kitchens, separate bedrooms, small dens, and their own private bathrooms. I thought that I had it about as good as it gets for a soldier deployed to Afghanistan, with my college dorm room and clean new shower and restroom facilities, which I shared with two dozen other men from six or eight troop-contributing nations. But I had forgotten about the people who lived and worked at the American Embassy.

"I heard one these guys refer to this as a hardship tour, because it's Afghanistan," Isabelle teased. But then we had to abruptly stop mocking the embassy staffers when the public affairs director Mike Stepp snuck up on us with a couple new members of his staff.

"What's up gang?"

"Same ole, same ole," Missy said.

Mike Stepped stepped aside and Anne Smedinghoff appeared.

"This is Anne," Mike said.

We all greeted her, but Charlie Church rose like a general had walked into the room, shaking hands with her firmly.

"I'm Charlie Church."

"Anne. Smedinghoff."

"Welcome to the big show, Anne. How long you been in country?"

"A couple months, actually."

"You like it so far?"

"Love it."

"Don't worry, it's still early," Isabelle said with a big smile on her face. But then she followed up quickly. "Just kidding. Welcome."

"Thanks," Anne said, and she matched Isabelle's smile.

It was extraordinary that all these people who came from different backgrounds and who were going through the same frustrations and separation anxiety—all of whom would rather be home than here—could get along and work so well together. Well, most of the time. The next night, walking back to our building with Isabelle Heyward at the end of the day—we lived in the same building, me on the first floor, Isabelle on the second floor—I realized we didn't get along as well as I had thought. She was quiet for the first minute, and walked ahead of me, like she didn't want to walk together.

"You okay? Am I depressing you with all my homesick talk?"

"No, that's not it," she snapped. "Other people are pissing me off."

"People we work with?"

"Yes, sir. I'm tired of people with their attitudes."

She then unloaded, one person at a time. One section didn't want to help another. She went after an Air Force lieutenant, who worked under my supervision, for being lazy and not pulling his weight, and a civilian woman who didn't work under my supervision, who had copped an attitude when Lieutenant Heyward had asked her to collaborate on a project. I realized that I had a new challenge on my hands, not just to handle my own anxieties by finally finding some emotional solid ground, but by being the leader in the office that I had not yet become. But every day was another day.

In the afternoon, NBC's Kabul-based correspondent, Atia Abawi, came to HQ ISAF. I took better care of her than she was accustomed to, moved her through the security gate in record time, and then walked her up to our office to meet some of the staff and renew acquaintances with others. We had met four years earlier, when she was new in Afghanistan and working for CNN, and I was still early in my first deployment. We were both different people back then, exuberant, optimistic, cheerful. She had come here—to the land of her forefathers—filled with hope for the future of Afghanistan. But four years here had deflated that bubbly optimism, and I could sense as we talked that she wouldn't be able to endure much more of the heartbreak.

"I'm so afraid we're going to fail here," she said.

"I won't let myself feel that way," I repeated—almost the same speech I had delivered to the Pakistani journalists recently. I told her about Dover, and Laura McGower, and the other mothers I had seen there. I told her about Laura McGower's daughter, and how I would like to find her some answers.

"I wish that too," she said. "But I've just seen too many failures, too many people who've had their hopes dashed. My dream is to come back here one day with Conor and our children and show them how much better Afghanistan is than it used to be because of what America and the other countries sacrificed. That's my hope, and I cling to it, somehow."

"Me too," I said.

She was heartbroken and melancholy, but she still had the beautiful smile I remembered from our first meeting four years earlier.

CHAPTER FIVE

THE SECRETARY OF defense visited Afghanistan in early December. I latched on to the group supporting his press corps hoping to shake his hand, and I just happened to be in the right place because when he walked up to the Yellow Building, I was standing at the door with a half dozen other ISAF officers. He had a strong firm grip that I liked, even though I didn't always agree with him politically. That didn't matter here. He was the boss. And he was here. That counted for a lot.

"Mr. Secretary," I said with a nod.

"Good to meet you, Colonel."

He was about to move forward and greet Charlie Church, but I pulled him back with a few words.

"We've met, sir."

He took a half step back toward me.

"Really, where?"

"On the ramp at Dover, early January 2010, when the bodies of your seven CIA officers returned from here."

There could be no doubt about the depth of his pain and memories from that day. Even though he had experienced so many remarkable days in his long and distinguished career—White House chief of staff, CIA director, secretary of defense—I knew the events of that day haunted him, as my memories of that day haunted me. We had little in common, but the secretary and I had that connection. I thought about that day all the time, and I didn't have the close personal and professional connection that he did.

"That was some day," he said. "One of the most memorable, and worst days, of my career."

He hesitated, reflected. I had inadvertently inserted a harsh memory on him that temporarily distracted him. Even Secretary Panetta could be stunned temporarily by a sucker punch, and I had thrown that sucker punch, purely by accident of course.

So, you were there?"

"Yes sir. I was the PAO."

He was still standing in front of me, so I kept talking.

"I worked with your team to set up that secure video feed. Then I set up the viewing area for the CIA employees and the families, parked the buses, and escorted some of the family members to the viewing area."

"That was a horrible day, but the Dover team gave us great support," he said.

Yes, we did, I thought.

"I don't often run into people who were also at Dover that day."

"Yes sir."

I had the impression he would've stayed and talked about that horrible day a little more, like perhaps talking about it would've provided us both some therapy. But, his time was in high demand and his schedule was tight. He moved past me and greeted Charlie Church, who was both composed and giddy at the same time. I think perhaps I stole a few seconds of Charlie's time with the secretary, but Charlie still savored the moment. He still fascinated me. Young and smart, he probably still had to pinch himself every so often. My mind quickly wandered away to a frigid day on the Dover tarmac.

Dover AFB, January 5, 2010

The AFMAO public affairs team got to the ramp well ahead of everyone else for this special dignified transfer. Our one consolation was that the CIA video van was parked on the ramp, and it gave us a place to get out of the cold.

The temperature hovered around freezing, but a brisk wind whipped across the tarmac, pushing the wind chill into the teens. We rolled out the stanchions and blocked off two areas, one for CIA employees and another for the families of the seven fallen CIA officers, exactly as we had outlined it. Then we waited, shivering, trying every possible method to shield ourselves from the relentless wind that roared straight down the tarmac—as it had for many DTs in the previous two months. We tapped our boots, danced a little, stood close to one another, and a few people at a time squeezed into the CIA production van parked a hundred feet from the aircraft. But then it was time.

The CIA employees started walking en masse toward the aircraft. As they approached, I looked into their solemn, shocked faces. I could read their minds. They couldn't believe that this could happen to the agency, seven of their own taken out by a Jordanian double-agent whom they thought would lead them to key insurgent leaders in Khost and close to the Afghanistan-Pakistan border. They were dressed in long, black overcoats, with gloves, hats, and scarves. They looked like the CIA agents I had seen on TV, hanging out at Langley, around Washington, in those stealthy intel conferences only special people were allowed to attend. They didn't look like field agents who moved in and out of Afghan villages, back and forth into Pakistan or Uzbekistan. They just looked like well-dressed people going to a funeral. Seven funerals.

I had no clue of their rank or seniority, so I just led those at the front of the procession to the front of the viewing area. Many lingered behind, pacing, shivering, wondering, but I had to cautiously usher them into the designated viewing area to make room for the buses, which started rolling onto the ramp minutes later. I started ushering in the buses, parking them close together. A few of the drivers strayed out of line, which blocked the walking path for family members in some of the buses. But we got the buses parked and stood while the entire AFMAO mortuary staff—all the funeral directors who normally rotated duty for the military DTs—climbed off the buses and began to lead the families to their designated viewing area. It took at least ten minutes to get the families in place. Some also wandered aimlessly, shocked and overwhelmed by the enormity of what had happened and what was before them. There were a lot of children and a few young teenagers. I knew that the team chief for the Afghanistan unit was a young woman in her mid or late thirties, with two or three small children, and when three small children were ushered to the head of the group, right up to the blue nylon rope that connected the stanchions, I knew most assuredly that those were the children of the female team leader. And I also knew, she being the senior agent, her body would come off the C-17 first.

With the families in place, the leadership marched onto the ramp, led by CIA director Panetta, Marine four-star general Cartwright, and a string of high-level civilians I didn't know or recognize. When the official party was in place, the Air Force carry team from AFMAO marched onto the ramp. Seconds later, they emerged from the back of the aircraft and walked slowly down the ramp, carrying the flag-draped transfer case containing the body of the fallen CIA team chief. Instantly, those three children leaning against the rope began to wail, and I began to shake more profusely, but braced myself for what was to come. There would be six more cases still, which would completely exhaust the five men and three women on the AFMAO carry team who had been selected to carry all seven cases from the aircraft to the awaiting transfer vehicles.

Each transfer took two or three minutes, so for close

to twenty minutes, three hundred people stood and shook against the freezing wind and the enormous sadness that enveloped the ramp at Dover and the proud and unshakable men and women of the Central Intelligence Agency. When the last transfer vehicle disappeared, and all the families were ushered again onto warm buses, and the CIA employees had walked slowly back to the passenger terminal, my team and I began to disassemble the stanchions while the CIA production team rolled up cable and stowed their gear. When I turned around and looked back toward their van, Mr. Panetta and General Cartwright were just a few feet from us. They thanked me and my team for our support and presented us with their coins. My NCOs got both coins but somehow, I missed getting Mr. Panetta's coin, but graciously accepted General Cartwright's coin. Then their handlers hurried them to sleek, private jets waiting on the tarmac nearby. Later that day, I heard mention of FOB Chapman for the first time.

The secretary of defense came back to me after he talked to Charlie Church. When I came back from that flashback, he was standing in front of me. Had it been a long time? I'm sure it was an eternity for his handlers.

"Did you get my coin?"

"Not at the time, sir. You were talking to one of my NCOs."

He pulled out his coin and buried it into my hand.

"This is my SecDef coin, of course. Thank you for your service, Colonel.

"Thank you, Mr. Secretary. And for your service, as well."

He stepped away again, past Charlie this time, and sure enough, his handlers looked aggravated with me. *Too bad*, I thought as that coin grew warm in my hand. He was, after all, just serving his country, like me. Except he had flown over here with a fifty-person entourage and got to hang out with Erin Burnett of CNN. He flew on a C-17, just like me, but lounged in the silver bullet, an airstream mobile home that fit snugly in the cargo bay of the giant aircraft and provided him comfortable sleeping quarters and privacy. He would also be going home for Christmas.

One of the reporters stepped up to me and asked my name, and if he could put me in his story.

"I'm Bob Firestone from the Associated Press," he said. "What did you and the secretary talk about?"

"Sir, I'm a PAO so I'd rather not be in your story, if that's okay."

"I understand. You too just looked like old friends."

"No, I just recalled an experience we shared together a few years ago. It was just a rare private moment with the secretary. I'll never get another opportunity like that."

"Sure, no problem. He just spent a long time with you."

"I'll give you this much."

He pulled out his notepad quickly.

"When he said, 'Glad to meet you,' I told him we had met before," I said carefully.

"Where?"

I paused, choosing my words carefully.

"On the ramp at Dover. That's all I can say. I just told him we had met before. I'd like to keep the circumstances of that meeting private."

"Okay. Can I write that you had a brief exchange with the secretary and recalled to him a previous meeting on the ramp at Dover?"

"Sure," I said, "but that's all."

He squinted to see my camouflaged nametape.

"Can I ask your first name and job title?"

"You know my name already,"

He looked puzzled.

"I'm Lieutenant Colonel Bristow Watson. You made me famous—or infamous around here—with the quote, 'General Allen returned to work on Wednesday.'"

He smiled. "Oh yeah . . . yep, that got a lot of ink."

The next day I sent Isabelle to Regional Command North with General Kinkel. She had been in Afghanistan almost five months and had not left Kabul. I had been to Mazar-e-Sharif twice in December of 2008 and wanted to give her the chance to get out of Kabul once before her deployment concluded. Besides, I was pretty sure General Kinkel and I would make a few trips together before my deployment was finished.

Mazar-e-Sharif, Afghanistan, December 6, 2008

On the ride back to Camp Marmal, I rode in the center hatch of the Fox, right behind the gunner in the forward turret. I crouched low in the opening, kept my head behind the iron protective plates, but could still see everything. Before we left the gunner told me to stay alert and signal him if I saw anything unusual. Unusual how? I thought. Like that old man carrying his belongings and his whole family on a huge flat car, pulled by a donkey? Or that burka-clad woman walking on a dusty road being trailed by a half dozen children?

The city of Mazar-e-Sharif was a sprawling, flat, brown city at the base of rolling brown hills. In the pictures, it's green with trees, but from the outskirts, I saw no green and no trees. When we got back to Camp Marmal, my face was covered with dirt and my sunglasses had a heavy dusty film across them. It must've looked pretty funny because Christoph Reuter, the German writer from Stern Magazine had to get a picture of me before I took off my glasses and wiped my face. Mazar-e-Sharif has a rich cultural heritage and history. The famous Blue Mosque is at the heart of the city, but it's not safe to visit for American and coalition troops. In my VIP quarters on the second night here (I had a VIP room reserved for the first night, but no one told me, so I slept in the tent), I read the brochure in the room that highlighted the area around Camp Marmal. On the ride back from the MES PRT today, crouched in the open hatch and looking out, I got a long and distant view of the city and all I saw was brown. The brochure shows pictures of the Blue Mosque, green grass, and trees, but from the hazy distance of my protected and armored perch, I saw no blue and no green. I did see a nicely paved section of road that connected two bumpy and rough roads between the base and the PRT. It would be nice to see this thoroughfare completed.

On my second and last night at Camp Marmal, I walked alone and looked up and the sky and thought how it looked the same as Texas. Does the moon look the same in Afghanistan as it does in South Carolina? If it's a half moon here, is it also a half moon back home, where my family might also look up and see it? The moon and the constellations were positioned in the same configuration as on those clear nights in Texas six weeks earlier. Enjoy that night sky, I thought to myself. Tomorrow it was back to Kabul and the smoke and haze of the city that blocks the view of the moon and stars. (Coincidentally, I was wrong about that, because on my third day back in Kabul, it was the clearest day since I had been there, and we could see the mountains clearly and at night we could actually see the moon and stars.) On this night, the moon provided enough light to ease my trek through the dark. German ingenuity took care of marking the path, with rows of floor lighting, similar to a movie theater, low, angled lights on each edge of the sidewalk, not visible from above but giving off just enough ambient light.

I actually enjoyed the solitude of walking alone, but the intense loneliness gripped me. The day before had been my daughter's birthday and I couldn't call her. The next day was my son's birthday, and I didn't feel like a factor in his life.

I felt like my family was a million miles away and drifting farther away each day. We were literally divided by half a world, and on this night, it felt like it.

It was easy to find some humor the next night, even with an important and forward-looking meeting wrapping the events of the evening. It was especially easy to poke fun at myself, and I think my colleagues on the press desk appreciated it sometimes when tensions were often very high. General Kinkel invited me to accompany him for a high-level media round table, with a four-star panel, as he called it. He said it was sponsored by the BBC, so I assumed it was at the BBC studio in downtown Kabul. I got all geared up and excited about making the drive downtown. Kabul on a Friday night, a sight I had probably not seen before. Of course, Kabul on a Friday night was like any town in America on a Monday night. But I still thought it would be an interesting drive. I had on my gloves, ballistic eye wear, and body armor. I even commented to me colleagues that I should've gone down to my room to get my prescription glasses just so I could see the sites of Kabul better.

We drove out the gate and turned right instead of taking our normal route, which was a left turn immediately after exiting the camp. We drove a hundred meters or so, then took a left turn into the Radio Television Afghanistan compound, directly across the street from our camp, adjacent to the US Embassy compound and not more than three hundred meters from where I slept every night! We were in the vehicles less than five minutes and had traveled a few hundred meters. But, the radio event was worth the trip, I remarked to some colleagues later. The two-hour radio broadcast—not surprisingly—turned out to be immensely more interesting than the drive. I had fully expected the excursion through Kabul to be the highlight. Luckily, the general was right. It was an all-star lineup that included a security adviser to the president of Afghanistan, two brave, outspoken Afghan women who spoke without fear, almost demanding more future opportunities for Afghan girls and women. Perhaps the star of the show, at least on paper, was Dr. Ashraf Ghani, a United States-educated Afghan leader who headed up the process of transitioning security and military operations from ISAF and NATO forces to Afghan forces. The room was crowded, so the ISAF support staff—the general's adviser, security team, and I—sat in a small control room across the hall from the studio and listened to the broadcast being beautifully translated from Dari to English by our interpreter, Temor. General Kinkel engaged enthusiastically with the entire Afghan panel. It was easy to be optimistic after the meeting. During the postshow greetings, Doctor Ghani shook my hand and called me "colonel." Of course, I didn't know then that he would be elected president of Afghanistan less than two years later.

After the two-hour live radio broadcast, we geared up, loaded up into three vehicles with our six armed commandos and drove back across the street to HQ ISAF. Back at the office, I wrote a humorous post about my Friday night drive through Kabul. The responses were predicable, but funny just the same.

"All dressed up and nowhere to go."

"Living on the edge."

And from my nephew, a former Army sniper with two tours in Afghanistan: "Oh, the daring and dangerous life you lead!"

I wouldn't call my life daring. Every day carried a certain degree of danger for all foreigners in this violent country, especially if you wore a coalition uniform. But when I posted stories about my experiences, or elaborated on my experiences in Facebook messages, emails, or online video chats, I was very careful not to compare my deployment to the real heroes out there. Those warriors lived in frequently attacked forward operating bases or combat outposts, patrolled towns and villages looking for insurgents, trained and mentored Afghan forces, and stood side by side with armed Afghans every day, knowing that one in every thousand—or maybe every ten thousand—would rather kill the ISAF soldier than work with him or her. I wasn't in Khost city, walking through a crowded and vulnerable market, attempting to force biometric scans on Afghan men that locals identified as having possible ties with the insurgency, and I especially wasn't staging daring night operations from otherwise safe and secure home bases like Bagram or the ISAF Joint Command headquarters at KAIA.

My job was neither daring nor dangerous, but it was necessary and important, and it got me quoted in all kinds of major international and American media outlets like the *Los Angeles Times* and the *Wall Street Journal*.

Some of the real heroes were those soldiers and marines— wounded warriors—who came back here early that December through a program called Operation Proper Exit, a privately funded, DoD-supported initiative to bring wounded warriors back to Afghanistan so they could leave again, but this time on their own terms. At first I thought it was rather trivial or too theatrical—why bring back warriors who were lucky to make it out alive the first time to the violent and unsecure land that had almost killed them the first time? But, when I took my first look at those wounded warriors and shook the first hand (an Army sergeant with a prosthetic leg), I understood. These brave American volunteer fighters deserved the option to leave this country sitting in web seating on a C-17 and not strapped to a litter, desperately looking at the place below their knee where their leg used to be.

I offered my support to the civilian public affairs officer at New Kabul Compound and got myself on part of the trip. They spent the first night at HQ ISAF, after getting a personal greeting from the commander and dinner in the VIP room of the main DFAC. The next morning, we met just after sunup to board Blackhawks for an hour-long flight to Forward Operating Base Shank, in the volatile Logar Province. A few of them had served there, been wounded near there, and had been treated by the medical staff there.

At Camp Bastion and Camp Leatherneck, the sprawling

American and British joint base in Helmand Province, a different group of marines had that look on their faces. They even toured the coalition hospital, where a few of them had spent some time under entirely different circumstances—when they didn't know if they would live or die, or ever walk again. One young soldier even got a special greeting from an Army nurse on her second tour here who had helped save his life three years earlier after his up-armored Humvee struck an IED. The soldiers and marines held a town hall meeting with fellow warriors and boldly recollected their deployments, and what they could remember from their last missions, when their combat careers had abruptly ended. They received a standing ovation when they stepped onto the makeshift stage. I watched the audience. I sensed an overwhelming respect. But I know some of those soldiers had to be thinking, *Please God, don't let that happen to me.* They wouldn't be human if they weren't thinking that.

I talked to one very young soldier—a specialist—who had two prosthetic legs that I could see, and many other injuries—hearing loss and extensive organ damage—that I couldn't see. He had lost count, but believed his next surgery, coming up in a few weeks, would be his forty-fifth. I couldn't imagine what kind of strength it took to endure that, what kind of fortitude it took to keep wearing the uniform of his military service and his country, and what kind of courage it had taken to come back here and face his demons. And then he stood in front of a group of fellow warriors and talked about it, and told them he had no regrets, but only gratitude that he was still alive and well enough to make the long trip back. He brushed away a few tears as he talked.

Since I was just along for the ride, and had no real duties on this trip (except to observe and learn in case I had to engage media about this extraordinary event later), I was able to be an admiring member of that town hall audience, part of the support staff with a listening ear when the specialist told me his story, and just another grateful officer who was glad we had young men like this in our United States

Armed Forces. The trip was short, but memorable. It took me to legendary places—like Camp Leatherneck—that I had only heard about, but never thought I'd ever visit. But more importantly, it gave me the privilege to spend time with some extraordinary soldiers and marines who were lucky enough not to pass through Dover on their way home. For that, I too was thankful.

Because I was part of his inner circle, General Kinkel always invited me to observe his stand-up interviews in front of the Yellow Building. Our translator and cultural adviser would come along too. While we waited for the general's military assistant to bring the journalist, the adviser, whom we called doctor—who had gotten his PhD in the Soviet Union before the Russian Invasion of 1980—would look around, at the camp, at the Destille Garden, and talk about his childhood.

"I played in the garden as a boy," he told the general.

"Oh, really?"

"Yes, I grew up only two miles from here," the doctor said.

I was a witness to the history of Afghanistan in 2012 that scholars and military historians would write about for years to come, but there were people entrenched in the history of Kabul when it was a great and thriving city, before communism and the Soviet invasion that I didn't understand in 1980 but understood only slightly better now. My only recollection of the Soviet invasion was that it boxed in President Jimmy Carter and forced the American boycott of the 1980 Olympics in Moscow. The Russians reciprocated and refused to come to Los Angeles in 1984. All because the big bad evil communist empire invaded Afghanistan, a country I don't think I had ever heard of prior to 1980.

The doctor was sixty-three years old, a fact I learned a few days later when he volunteered to be interviewed for a story in *AARP: The Magazine*, which I also thought was for old people, but the organization opened up the membership to fifty-plus-year-olds, so it had a wide membership.

For one of General Kinkel's interviews, I went to the main gate, met the journalists, cleared them through security and escorted them. That walk was one of the most interesting five minutes of my entire deployment.

My history here went back four years. The doctor's history, and an Afghan journalist I had met on my previous tour, Shahir Zahine's, history went back more than sixty years.

HQ ISAF, Kabul, Afghanistan, January 2009

After the journalists traded in their cell phones and credentials for a visitor badge, we passed through the first of two turnstiles. I gave my usual brief tour to journalists as we approached the Yellow Building. I had already warmed up to Melek Zahine during the sign in, where she displayed her American passport and talked about being born in Turkey, which fascinated me and the Turkish lieutenant assisting me. Born in Turkey and raised in Connecticut, she now lived in Kabul with Shahir, her Afghan husband whom she had met in Pakistan. A real world traveler. That in itself was interesting enough. At the gate, I had asked to see her American passport more out of curiosity than necessity, pretending to use it for her identity check. Every page in her passport was stamped. She had been everywhere, it seemed. Shahir headed up the Killid Group, a multi-faceted communications and publishing corporation that advocates for women and publishes English language and Afghan language publications. They were very impressive. In the weeks to come, they would not only be the first Afghan journalists to get one-on-one interviews with the ISAF commanding general, but they would be sought out for advice on how to reach the Afghan people by engaging the Afghan media.

I carried on with the Zahines like old friends. I told them

about the Yellow Building like I knew something of this place. Mr. Zahine jumped in politely.

"Yes, I've been here before," he said. I thought he was talking about the ISAF headquarters, but he was talking about another era, in another life.

"This used to be a military training headquarters," Melek said, and again I misunderstood. I thought she was talking about the Taliban, because I had heard the Yellow Building had been a Taliban palace and headquarters.

She corrected me again.

"It was once an Afghan military complex, before the Taliban, before the Russians, before war came to this country. You know, before the Taliban and the Russians, there was an Afghan government," she reminded me. "Kabul was once a beautiful and prosperous city, when Shahir was growing up here."

I sensed a touch of sadness in her voice, that sadness that Afghans over the age of forty most likely feel when they think about what Kabul was like before the Russians had come in 1980. (Again, what I remember about that was it kept the Americans out of the 1980 Olympics, followed by the ripple effect of the Soviets boycotting the 1984 Olympic Games in Los Angeles. The Russian invasion of Afghanistan was so much more to people like Shahir Zahine.)

"Someday, Shahir will have to tell you about Kabul."

I thought, Yes, that's a story I'd like to hear. But all I could think of to say was, "I know Kabul was once a prosperous and beautiful city, I've read The Kite Runner twice and seen the movie several times." She wasn't totally unimpressed with my sophomoric statement.

"It's just a book, but Kabul was really like that once," she said. They reached the door, and I didn't have a chance to hear more. But she had said so much in just a few minutes.

Just two days after the Zahines came to HQ ISAF (as journalists), they came again for a one-on-one interview with the commander of ISAF and US Forces. Shahir Zahine was about to become the first Afghan journalist to interview the commander. But before that came a dose of reality and humiliation. While the Zahines were entering the compound, other Afghan journalists were coming to the headquarters for another engagement. They would be subject to the scanner, so because there were other Afghan journalists besides Mr. Zahine, all of them were put through the security body scanner.

I had a special badge that allowed me to escort journalists onto the compound without being searched, accepting the burden myself of vouching for the potential security risk. I could've used that authority to spare Shahir and Melek the degradation of being searched, but when we did that, the Afghan journalists complained about the special treatment westerners received. So, embarrassed, I asked Shahir to stand in front of the scanner while I moved his wife—with her American passport—straight through the turnstile. I didn't want to subject him to that but didn't want to treat him differently than the other Afghan journalists, and I could never risk bringing Afghan journalists I didn't know onto the NATO command headquarters without all the security precautions. Mr. Zahine was cooperative, but I could see and sense the offense this caused him, especially knowing that Shahir had come here as a teenager many times—before the Russians and the Taliban—to do what teenagers whose city is not at war do, swim, play sports, hang out with other kids. Now, he was chairman of a major media conglomerate, with his distinguished goatee. He didn't look like the headdress-wearing Mujahedeen freedom fighter of another life in the photo of him Melek showed me later.

After the scanner, I spent the next minute apologizing,

but Melek told me I had no reason to apologize, and so did Shahir, although he surely felt the burn of humiliation.

It was interesting how no matter where I went, I always found people easy to get attached to. I had met the Zahines twice and felt like they were close friends. Melek had actually lived in Charleston for seven years. I had lived there twenty years earlier. I knew the "small world" cliché was overused, but I was in Afghanistan with a fascinating woman born in Turkey, raised in America, now married to an Afghan man and one-time freedom fighter, living in Kabul, and yet at times in our lives Melek Zahine and I had lived in the same South Carolina city. I considered it one of those head-scratchers. I'd spent Christmas Eve that year with a total stranger who just happened to be born in the same hospital as me. Another head-scratcher.

On our second walk from the main gate to the Yellow Building, Shahir told me again that in the 1970s this compound was an Afghan military club and recreation center, with soccer fields and swimming pools. (The soccer field was still there . . . not sure what happened to the swimming pools.) He had come here with his friends whose fathers were officers of the Afghan military.

"It must be kind of interesting and perplexing to come back here in 2009 and see what the compound is," I said.

On Christmas Eve 2012, I walked alone to the embassy to eat dinner at the apartment of a young couple, who had invited all their church friends to their home. It was a nice evening, but not as memorable as the last Christmas Eve I had spent here. We ate a splendid "Sunday-type" dinner with roast and mashed potatoes, sang Christmas carols, and read from the Bible the story of the Savior's birth.

It was a warm Christmas Eve, but after I made the trek back

to HQ ISAF, I spent the rest of the evening thinking about my first Christmas in Afghanistan.

December 24, 2008
Kabul, Afghanistan

I honestly can't remember the last time I worked on Christmas Eve, but I'm sure it's been a number of years. But, today felt almost like any other day, at least until the afternoon and evening. All day my colleagues teased me about making sure I had some mistletoe for the public affairs office dinner tonight, so we tried printing a picture of mistletoe, but as usual, our equipment was inadequate. So, I delivered a stirring rendition of "I Saw Mama Kissing Santa Claus (Underneath the Mistletoe Last Night)" to my Turkish friends this afternoon. They were puzzled, to put it mildly.

Since I'm away from my family on Christmas for the first time since 1980, I feel like these people I'm with now are my family, at least for this Christmas. My family consists of American soldiers, sailors, airmen, and marines, Brits, Turkish colleagues, Australians, Germans, Italians, Dutch, and several dozen folks of other nationalities. I even met my first Austrian in the camp and told him about my son serving half of his LDS church mission there. He said there are two Austrians at HQ ISAF.

Every part of Christmas Eve exceeded my expectations. At six o'clock tonight several hundred people from a few dozen nations gathered in Destille Garden and braved forty-degree temperatures to celebrate Christmas. I had been looking forward to this candlelight Christmas Eve service because I wanted some part of this week to feel like Christmas. Tonight felt like Christmas Eve. We started off singing "O Come All Ye Faithful." If I was home at my parents' house on Christmas Eve, we might sing this hymn of faith and celebration. Then Admiral Borsboom took the podium and read the first scripture. While he read from the Bible about the birth of Christ, we could clearly hear the Muslim call to prayer outside the walls of the ISAF Compound. This was truly going to be a unique and memorable Christmas.

Then the faith choir, mostly Americans but with some Dutch and Brits mixed in, broke into the familiar "Go Tell it on the Mountain," and for a few minutes I was back in the Southern United States, listening to the vibrant beat of a black church choir in rural South Carolina.

Then we sang "O Come, O Come Emmanuel." Wow, it was like a two-hundred-person choir was singing. I've sang that hymn with the church choir in Columbia. I've heard the Mormon Tabernacle Choir perform it. But even if I'd had the world's best choir ringing in my ears, I don't think at this moment in my life, these hymns that celebrate the birth of Christ could could have delivered a more meaningful message than on a cold evening in Kabul. I've always felt and tried to understand the deep meaning of this hymn, but never have the lyrics we sang as the second verse held so much meaning for me, as we try to bring Heaven's peace to this battered land.

O come, O come Emmanuel,
And ransom captive Israel,
That mourns in lonely exile here,
Until the son of God appear.

O come, desire of nations, bind
All peoples in one heart and mind;
Bid envy, strife, and quarrels cease,
Fill all the world with Heaven's peace.

Rejoice! Rejoice!
Emmanuel shall come to thee, O Israel.

As I looked around, I realized we had local journalists actually covering the celebration. They were from Reuters and the Associated Press, but they were actually Afghans. Afghans covering a Christian celebration. Celebrating Christmas in downtown Kabul, Afghanistan. Even being so far away from home and missing my family desperately, I felt like I was among family. And even with all these people from many distant nations and being in a distant land, I stood and celebrated Christmas Eve next to a man from Charleston, South Carolina, born in the same city I was born in, Columbia. It really is a small world, isn't it?

The chaplain spoke about the Christmas truce of 1914, when Germans and British put down their weapons for one evening and celebrated together. That is what we seek, not only on this night, but during our entire deployments here in Afghanistan—"Peace on earth and goodwill toward men." I still remember many Christmases in my life. When I was in Australia, as a young missionary away from home for the first time, alone and homesick, a Russian family received us into their home and set deep in my heart a lasting memory. And I have many wonderful recollections of Christmas when my children were young. But tonight, as I celebrate this Christmas of all Christmases, in Afghanistan, I know will never forget this evening as long as I live.

In closing, the chaplain announced that we would sing "Silent Night." But first he told the story of how the hymn was written. Of course, it was not written as "Silent Night," but as "Stille Nacht," by Austrians Franz Gruber and Joseph Mohr near Salzburg in 1818.

On Christmas Eve of 1818, Mohr, an assistant pastor at St Nicholas, showed Gruber a six-stanza poem he had written in 1816. He asked Gruber to set the poem to music. The church organ had broken down, so Gruber produced a melody with guitar arrangement for the poem. The two men sang "Stille Nacht" for the first time at Christmas Mass in St Nicholas Church while Mohr played guitar and the choir repeated the last two lines of each verse.

The chaplain turned down the lights, and everyone lit their candles, and Dutch navy lieutenant commander Theo Klootwijc sang the first verse of the hymn the way it was originally sung, in German.

CHAPTER SIX

I WOKE UP early enough on Christmas morning 2012 in Kabul to spend Christmas Eve with my children and grandchildren in America, spread across the country in three major cities but accessible by the miracle of FaceTime. I felt like I had not missed my wife as much on this deployment—I had missed her desperately during my first deployment—only because I knew that no matter how slow the clock seemed to tick, the time would pass, and I would get home to her. But I felt like I had abandoned my children and grandchildren, although we had grown accustomed to me being away for Christmas. All three of my deployments had fallen during the same part of the year—early November until April or May (March for the Dover deployment).

On Christmas Day in Kabul, it was warm, and I talked about how we played golf in South Carolina during the Christmas holidays. When I was walking back from lunch with a group of my colleagues, I even stopped to practice my golf swing with an imaginary 9-iron. But even trying to be jovial, it was my first really difficult day since that depressing election day when Barack Obama had been reelected to a second term and Colonel Daniels had told me we had no chance to make a positive difference in Afghanistan.

Two days later, early in the morning, it started to snow. It snowed all day, a wet heavy snow. Early in the day I stood out on our back deck and watched the big flakes hit the picnic table. *Splat*! Like a large, saturated noodle hitting the ground. By the afternoon, three or four inches of snow had fallen. I bundled up in my cold-weather gear, courtesy of the American taxpayer, and hiked out to the gate to meet an Associated Press reporter who was doing a special story for AARP about "seasoned" soldiers in Afghanistan. I had been calling this the "old people" story for the past week. He interviewed our Afghan American cultural adviser and interpreter, the doctor, who had been born and raised in Kabul, educated by the Soviets, then had eventually immigrated to America, where he had lived for the past thirty years among the Afghan population in Northern California. Now he was back, with his hopes and dreams and visions for Afghanistan. At sixty-three, he knew soon he would return to America, probably never to return again. But for now, he wanted to try one last time to make a difference for his homeland.

Later, as darkness began to set in—it was not yet five o'clock—when we were outside in a blinding snowstorm taking photos of an old colonel, I noticed a young Afghan man trying to shove and maneuver small plastic dumpsters down the road through the slush and ice, struggling and freezing while I stood bundled up and warm in all the cold-weather gear the Air Force had issued me. He had on a light wind-breaker type jacket and no hat or gloves. I made conversation with him for a few seconds, then realized just being friendly wouldn't keep his hands warm. I ran upstairs to my office where we were stockpiling donated gloves and coats to deliver to destitute Afghan children in Kabul orphanages, snatched the two biggest pairs of gloves I could find and ran back down the stairs. I helped him lift one of those rolling dumpsters onto a concrete slab and then pulled the gloves from my cargo pocket. He first attempted to pull on the red pair of women's gloves, and was determined to make them fit, no matter how odd they looked on him. Then he tried the gray pair and managed to push his cold, red, wet hands into those gloves. He gave me back the red gloves, placed his right hand flat across his chest—the symbol of friendship and gratitude, and thanked me several times.

A few minutes later, I saw him struggling to haul heavy black trash bags over his back, like Santa Claus, but he was wearing his gloves and smiling.

"Do you have a wife?" I asked.

"Yes," he replied.

I retrieved the red gloves from the cargo pocket of my pants and stuffed them inside his jacket.

"For your wife."

He took his right hand off the heavy bags and again placed it flat across his chest.

"Thank you, sir. Thank you," he said over and over.

"You're welcome," I said. "I hope you can stay warm out here."

"Thank you, sir," he said again. "I never forget you."

He said he would never forget me, and perhaps he meant it. Take that, Colonel Daniels. Maybe they do care.

On a Sunday morning, the same Dutch photographer from the snowstorm a few evenings earlier made a subsequent visit to HQ ISAF determined to capture more unique images for the AARP article. I had researched him some since his previous visit and discovered that he was not your average photographer, but a recognized and acclaimed photojournalist with a distinguished reputation as a wartime documentarian. He was well-known for his gritty photos of Afghan life and work photographing the momentous challenges facing soldiers in the Afghan National Army. He had taken thousands of photos of war-torn cities and war-ravaged people. He was part of a group of talented, brave photographers documenting life in Afghanistan. Every caption began with "The war is not over . . ." I pictured Joel out there embedding with the ANA, in remote Afghan villages, on the battlefield, and thought how bored he must now be, on assignment for the American Association of Retired People (old farts) collecting portraits of "seasoned" soldiers at HQ ISAF. One day he's embedded with the ANA along the Pakistan border, really asserting his considerable skill as a photographer, the next day he's at the chapel service on HQ ISAF, taking photographs of the sergeant major playing bass guitar in the Rock Chapel band! Everybody has to make a living and a job is a job. Plus, AARP probably paid pretty well. They paid me $275 in the mid-1980s to write a short piece about an elderly widow who made splendid, brightly colored kites out of cloth. Those would've been a huge hit in Afghanistan, where kite-flying had returned after being outlawed by the Taliban.

Joel and I meandered to the weekly memorial service, where more than a hundred other soldiers and civilians from at least two dozen nations had gathered around the circle of national flags to pay tribute to ISAF service members lost in the past week. The ceremony started moments after the commander of ISAF and US Forces exited the Yellow Building and took his place at the head of a formation of ISAF generals, plus the command sergeant major.

After the chaplain said a prayer and stated the purpose of the gathering, an American Army colonel read the names of a Navy SEAL commander—who was rumored to have died by suicide—and an Army sergeant killed by an IED blast in southern Afghanistan on Christmas Eve, the same day as an American civilian contractor whose death was widely reported by news organizations. Since there were only Afghan and American casualties in the past week, an Afghan National Army general followed the American colonel, and stood with strength and dignity in front of the entire group to honor the members of his army who had died in battle in the past week. But he did something remarkable first.

"The people of Afghanistan give our sincere condolences to these brave coalition forces who gave their lives for the security of Afghanistan," he said in beautifully accented, sincere English. "On behalf of our country, we thank these soldiers for their sacrifice in defense of Afghanistan."

I wished all those Gold Star mothers and young widows I had stood with at Dover on cold days and nights like this one could've heard this humble Afghan general offer his thanks for so much precious blood spilled. I know it would make people like Laura McGower feel a little better. It made me feel better. Then the Afghan general concluded by paying tribute to members of his own army—

twenty-four of them—who had died in the past week defending their homeland. I was moved by his words and by the sacrifices being made by his own army. During my first deployment here, when far fewer coalition forces were dying, I often wondered if the Afghan people really appreciated the monumental sacrifices being made, the blood being spilled, to try and bring some measure of security and hope to this country. At Dover, I had seen those sacrifices much closer, in the faces of grieving parents, young widows, and broken siblings. President Karzai's recent offer of condolences during an interview with my friend Atia Abawi was conditional. But today, an Afghan general had stood before several hundred coalition members and paid tribute to a pair of Americans who had died in this strange and foreign land. *Finally*, I thought, *someone has said thank you, and meant it.*

Just the night before, the body of that young Georgian soldier who had gone missing ten days earlier was found in southwestern Afghanistan. The next week his name would be read along with at least one US Marine who had died of his wounds the day before, after he and two fellow marines had hit an IED. It was likely a few names would be added before the memorial on the following Sunday.

In episode four of *Band of Brothers*, "Replacements," when the American forces jump into Holland and start liberating those war-torn Dutch cities, the grateful citizens shower them with gratitude as liberators. The beautiful Dutch women hug and kiss the American and British liberators, and many offer—and give up—their virginity in gratitude. It was interesting how during two Afghan deployments I had worked closely with the Dutch and the Germans, including on my first deployment when I worked with, advised, and traveled frequently with a Dutch admiral. What's more amazing is that now I work with, advise, and travel with a German general, whom I've grown to have great respect and affection for, and whose personal protection team keeps me safe when I move around Kabul with their general.

Will there come a time in Afghanistan when the people will

treat Americans and the other coalition forces as the liberators of Afghanistan? I know the women won't throw themselves at us and kiss us, it's not their culture, but will coalition troops ever get to feel that same sense of heroics, as the liberators of this people? We have attempted to be their liberators, but will we feel like that, and will the people look at us that way? Maybe the upcoming meeting between President Karzai and President Obama would help answer that question.

President Hamid Karzai. Easy to love, easy to hate—just depends on what day it is, and what he's said or done on that given day. In Washington, he thanked American forces for training the Afghan army. In an interview with Atia Abawi last month, he thanked American soldiers and their families for their great sacrifices, but his praise was conditional, and the thanks was directed only to those fallen soldiers and their families who came here to protect the Afghan people. Well, that's a huge part of the campaign, but only part of it. What about rooting out terrorism so 9/11 won't happen again, in the United States, or England, or some other land? What about training Afghan soldiers and police so they can secure their own country? What about all the hospitals, roads, and bridges that have been built, wells that have been dug and fresh water provided, food and supplies that have been delivered? The new Australian brigadier threw out to a group of media numbers some numbers I had not heard before. More than $10 billion in equipment and supplies had been delivered to the Afghan army and police, and no doubt most of that enormous amount of money came from the American taxpayer.

I was reading a book called *The Only Thing Worth Dying For*, about the fight against the Taliban in southern Afghanistan in the months after 9/11. The featured players were eleven US special forces warriors—including Major Bolduc, who was here at HQ ISAF now as Colonel Bolduc. He had just been informed of his upcoming selection to the rank of brigadier general. Like the generals in Afghanistan now, he earned that star on the battlefields, either here or in Iraq, like our own, Brigadier General Steph Twitty. Real generals, who earned it the old-fashioned way, in combat. But the star of the book I was reading was an emerging hero of Afghanistan politics and independence, the man who rallied the Pashtun tribal leaders against the Taliban, an educated and brilliant revolutionary named Hamid Karzai. In 2001, he was on a first-name basis with the American special forces captain he fought beside. In January of 2013, President Hamid Karzai—the biggest newsmaker in the world that week—was in Washington to meet with President Barack Obama, who by default of being American president is labeled the most powerful leader in the world. Their discussions focused on American-Afghan relations that will shape Afghanistan in the post–2014 era. Hamid Karzai, who, before he was the interim leader of Afghanistan and later its president for the past eight years, was a tribal leader who rallied the Pashtuns in southern Afghanistan against the Taliban. He had been the Taliban spokesman some years earlier but had rebelled against the brutal regime to become the exiled leader of what would become the uprising in the south. While the Northern Alliance were routing the Taliban in a siege of Kabul, Karzai, who would have been captured or killed by the Taliban before American covert operators extracted him from southern Afghanistan, was re-inserted into the mountains of Uruzgan Province with eleven US special forces troops and CIA spooks to stage an insurgency, first by taking Tarin Kowt and then waging war against the Taliban stronghold of Kandahar. In 2001, Karzai and the US special operators were the insurgents—the term was so noble then. The insurgency was against the Taliban regime. Now, today, the insurgents fight against Karzai and the Afghan government. Love him or hate him, he will go down in history as an extraordinary figure in modern Afghanistan history.

General Twitty joined in about how Karzai was lucky to be alive and how we had "saved his ass" with that daring extraction in 2001, and how short Karzai's memory can be sometimes. Charlie

Church threw out the question, "What if Massoud had lived and Karzai had been assassinated back in 2001, how would the last eleven years have been different?" The Afghans I talked to said Ahmad Shah Massoud had no personal agenda, was not corrupt, and only had the good of Afghanistan in his heart. Karzai is said to have no blood on his hands, but corruption is believed to flow through his family like winding rivers. He blamed America for making his family corrupt. But, back to the question. What if the Taliban had gotten Karzai in the mountains of southern Afghanistan in 2001? And what if Massoud had surrounded himself with a more able security force and had not been killed by suicide bombers posing as journalists? Good question. But, that's like saying what if President Kennedy, or Martin Luther King had lived, how would America have been different?

I know I admired President Karzai in 2013 much less than the 2001 freedom fighter Hamid Karzai. What happened to that Karzai, and could we please have the old Karzai back?

I had become a prisoner to the press desk for the past five or six weeks and had not been able to free myself from it except for those walks to the Embassy. So, when General Kinkel invited me to accompany him for an interview at Ariana television, it was the proverbial no-brainer. He didn't have to ask me twice. Secured in the back seat of the lead Land Cruiser, with the Germans in charge of the driving and protection, I was free to sightsee and talk to Temor, our interpreter. I asked him early in the drive if Ariana was near or far, and he said far. Thank goodness. I didn't want another one of those thirty-second trips. The weather was beautiful, and the people of Kabul were out en masse. The drive looked familiar, and as we got closer, I realized I had been there before, four years earlier with the Dutch admiral. We passed the Kabul Zoo and TV Hill, and I knew we were in the vicinity of the Serena Hotel, but I couldn't find it. On a main road on the south side of TV Hill, I looked across some open fields toward a mountain range and remembered the view exactly from four years earlier. It was a surreal feeling, like I had just been here. For a moment, the time between my Afghanistan deployments seemed compressed, and the final months of my first deployment seemed like the months just before arriving here a second time.

When we reached the compound, the German commandos steered the vehicles into a rutted, potholed side street.

"The road is not so good," my gunner understated drastically, as we bounced along for twenty or thirty meters until they brought the vehicle to a welcomed halt.

We egressed the vehicles and walked about fifty meters to the main entrance. That was liberating, actually walking down a Kabul street! It was muddy and icy, and I just about took a spill, but I felt an odd, big-breath freedom from the security and safety of the high walls of HQ ISAF and the armored vehicles that caged me. At the compound entrance, we stood out on the sidewalk and argued for a minute about how many of the general's close protection team would be allowed inside. All of them, Temor insisted. That minor dispute resolved, we hiked through the cave-like entrance and emerged inside the compound. Standing outside the main building, Temor had another dispute with this same security chief—whom we quickly found out wasn't in charge—about personal protectors and weapons inside the building. Temor said the general's protection team was a *red line* and asked to see the actual man in charge. The general manager appeared a minute later and welcomed us with open arms. We were all admitted, except one of the close protection team commandos who chose to remain in the courtyard to maintain exterior surveillance.

The general manager led us upstairs to the spacious office of the senior vice president, an American whom I immediately recognized from a church meeting I had attended at Camp Eggers six weeks earlier. (I thought, *maybe he'll hire me as a producer for Ariana TV after I retire, since I have no job waiting for me after this deployment.*) He graciously welcomed the general and his team, then led us down to the studio for the interview. It looked different from four years ago, but after the interview I walked into the control room and knew immediately I had sat in that control room and watched the technicians work, four years earlier. Where there had once been a window—I had sat in master control and watched Admiral Borsboom—today there was a piece of paper taped over the glass and a wooden facade built as a backdrop for one of their other programs.

When the interview was over, the American senior vice president escorted us on a tour of the compound. In the radio production facility, he introduced us to a young Afghan journalist named Abiseen.

"This young man is one of our heroes," the American said.

"Really, how so?" asked General Kinkel.

"Well, about four months ago—"

"Three and a half," corrected his Afghan producer and translator.

"Yeah, I guess about three and a half months ago, this young man was shot, four times, by the Taliban. They left him for dead, but luckily, he survived."

General Kinkel put his hand across his chest. "I'm so glad to see you're okay," he said. "Thank you."

The senior VP further explained that the young man was shot simply because he was a journalist but had miraculously survived and had just returned to work in the past few weeks. General Kinkel again acknowledged the young man's courage. I quickly scribbled down a few notes and looked him over for obvious signs of his wounds. As we walked away, he followed for a half dozen steps and I noticed he walked with a pronounced limp.

We backtracked into the courtyard and the tour abruptly ended. While we had been in the compound, the general's vehicle had been maneuvered and repositioned inside the compound, so he was geared up in his vehicle within seconds. Temor and I walked out the gate and down the same side street, slipping and sliding on frozen mud until we reached our vehicle, parked on the street. Again, I enjoyed the walk. Children approached us and Temor scolded them and tried to keep them away from our vehicles. The German driver pulled away from the curb carefully with the children still trying to clutch the door handles and mirrors.

On the return trip to HQ ISAF, we drove the same route I remembered from four years before, beside the Kabul River and through a vibrant part of the city. I had that sensation of compressed time again, like nothing had happened since the last time I had made this drive, with the Dutch close protection team and leading the vehicle carrying their principal, the Dutch two-star admiral who was now chief of the Dutch navy. We passed the Serena Hotel, and a flood of memories came back to me of the first time I had met Monika Winters. Our talented German drivers successfully avoided careless pedestrians who wandered aimlessly in front of our vehicles, and then delivered us safely back to the security of HQ ISAF.

Putting my life in the hands of the Germans was such an interesting dichotomy. At the very beginning of *Band of Brothers* Episode Nine, "Why We Fight," the men of Easy Company talk about the Germans and how many were just young kids like the American soldiers—just doing their job and fighting for what they thought was right. One of the men said, "Maybe we might've had a lot in common. Maybe he liked to hunt and fish, like me. Maybe under different circumstances we might've been good friends." Now, under different circumstances, I rode with a German close protection team and their general, my life completely in their hands, my military rank subordinate to his. And interesting enough, although their top priority would always be to take a bullet for their general, if required, I was pretty sure they would put their lives on the line to protect me too. Circumstances were certainly different, and now, the Germans and I were good friends. In fact, I considered General Kinkel one of my very closest and respected friends and colleagues in the camp. He had invited me into his inner circle very early in the deployment, and I had reciprocated by sharing with him some personal details of my life. When news from home made me stumble at times and I was unprepared for the prep sessions ahead of his media engagements, he recognized that something was amiss and cut me some slack. Besides my roommate, he was about the only one I expressed my concerns to. I couldn't imagine any circumstances that could make us enemies.

The next time General Kinkel traveled—to Kabul International Airport for an orientation of Afghan Air Force training—I wasn't with him. He had invited me to travel with his team, but I couldn't make the one-day trip because of commitments on the press desk. At the end of the day, his military assistant, Lieutenant Colonel Marc, couldn't wait to tell me about what I had missed. When he approached me—a huge smile stretching across his face—I was busy working on a pressing deadline. But he loomed over my desk, camera in hand, waiting to taunt me with the photographs from their flight in the Russian-made MI-17 Afghan Air Force helicopter. When I came to a stopping point in my current task, he started scrolling through the photos on his camera phone.

"This is us in the back of the helo," he said. Yes, it was definitely the German team in the back of the helicopter.

"This is the terrain," and he displayed a fascinating photo of a tall plateau bordered by jagged cliffs.

I don't think I purposely looked bored—envious maybe—but he started scrolling through the pictures more quickly.

"Wait! It gets better," he said, holding my attention.

Yep, it got better. Next were two photos of the stunning German sergeant named Steffi (whose last name I never learned), who had joined the general's close protection team after Christmas. Then, as if I needed further taunting, the next photo was the general occupying the gunner position, manning the.50-cal and firing at rocks and dirt below. Then, of course, there was a photo of Marc on the gun as well. I looked up at him and he flashed a *one-upped the American* smile, but I hastened to take some credit for the extraordinary day.

"It's a good thing I advised the general to get out more and gain more personal experiences to illustrate with personal anecdotes the progress we're making when he addresses the media," I reminded him. He heartily agreed.

Isabelle Heyward went home at the end of January. She had been wearing down for months, so it was time. She received a Defense Meritorious Service Medal and was applauded by the staff and leadership for working at a level beyond her rank—lieutenant junior grade, United States Navy. As anxious as she was to finally go home, in the hours before her departure it was like she just couldn't, or wouldn't, leave. She kept thinking of extra work to do. I know leaving behind the team was bittersweet. I have felt it before, and I would feel it again. Just minutes before she geared up and climbed into one of the vehicles in her convoy, she stood in the media operations center and stared at her desk and computer. She didn't know I was behind her, observing her final moments as an operator on the ISAF press desk. When she broke from her trance and turned as I approached, I saw her wipe a tear from her face.

"It's weird, but you're gonna miss this, aren't you?"

"Yes, I am, sir," she acknowledged. Then a smile spread across her face. "But I am so glad to be going home!"

During the previous few days, my ultra-liberal daughter had engaged me in a spirited—and sometimes nasty—exchange on America's motives in the "war on terror." She initiated this debate by sending me a ten-year-old article by a feminist anthropologist that made the argument the United States went to war in Afghanistan to save Afghan women from the evils of strict Islamic law by imposing our flawed western values on them. I tried desperately to find some objective information to send her that would at least bring her back to the middle, knowing that she might end up spending her entire professional career necessarily collaborating with people or governments with whom she disagreed, but on whom she might depend for funding. It would very likely be the evil American government that would eventually provide a vehicle to invoke her activism to benefit the people she would be attempting to help.

I wished desperately she could be virtually with me when I geared up today and drove through the ragged streets to a Kabul radio station, a dark, gloomy, and annoying snow shower obscuring the route. When we arrived there, our gracious hosts sat with us at a large conference table to prepare for a radio interview. The tea was placed right in front of us. Two Afghan women sat at the table with us, including a firm-looking woman at the head of the table opposite General Kinkel, me, and his interpreter. It didn't take me more than a minute or two to remember why experiences like this embedded in my memory as the most interesting and favorite part of the deployment, hoping that I could accurately surmise that Afghan society might someday mirror the growth and development I see in the Afghan media. The young chief editor, sitting beside the woman at the end of the table, started the meeting by welcoming us. In his reciprocating opening remarks, General Kinkel started with a question.

"Is the glass half-full or is it half-empty?" he asked. The young editor, Najib, took the question, but answered it in his own way.

"First, let me thank our international friends for trying to help us bring peace and security to our country. We thank you."

He thanked us first. Then warned us. "But transition must take place in our country by our own people."

"We agree," General Kinkel interjected.

"Yes, we cannot depend on foreign forces forever. Afghanistan is for Afghans."

He could not have said it better. He was young, educated, the future of Afghanistan. He said his colleagues worried about post–2014, something no one had talked about two or three years ago. When he was done, we got down to talking about the issues—Afghan security forces, equipment, the Afghan air force. The general provided long, detailed answers and explanations.

When I thought the prep session was over and it was time to relocate to the studio, the woman spoke . . . and spoke . . . and spoke. She was aggressive, and I could sense some hostility, even in a language I didn't speak. The Afghan version of my sweet daughter. When she finished after five minutes, the interpreter shook his head.

"Six questions," Temor said to the general. "I'm not sure where to start. I'm lost in the middle of nowhere," he said, putting a humorous spin on what I thought was an *English is not my first language explanation*. He eventually collected himself, arranged the notes in his head, then finally started translating.

"Why didn't you start building the Afghan Air Force ten years ago? Logar was safer three years ago than it is now. Why? Why do you repel the Taliban in an area and then not follow them and defeat them? Why do you allow illegal armed groups to threaten the people? Why are the nations going to take all their weapons back to their countries? Why don't they leave the weapons here in Afghanistan with the Afghan forces?"

All good questions. She was tough! But General Kinkel was neither deterred nor intimidated. He answered all of her questions without trying to force the impression that we had *all* the answers.

Again, I thought we were finished, but then one of the men asked a few questions, in perfect English, using the word *interject* a few times.

"Will you leave like the Russians?" The general assured him we would not, that the international community would not abandon Afghanistan. Then he asked why, when coalition forces had pledged to leave, did the Taliban still attack the foreign forces? General Kinkel answered a question with a question.

"Why do they fight you? Why do they fight Afghans? On the battlefield, the insurgents can no longer challenge coalition forces. So they fight Afghans, your forces, your civilian populations. Why are they fighting their own brothers and sisters?"

And with that, the prep session ended.

I didn't make it into the studio because a feisty Al Jazeera reporter called General Kinkel and demanded a statement immediately about the transfer of detainees from US forces to Afghan detention centers. The general handed me the phone and went into the studio. I stayed in the reception area and steered her call to the ISAF press desk. After I finished the call, I posed for photos with a couple of the Afghan journalists at the facility. Najib, the young facilitator, walked through the reception area and I asked him the "half-full or half-empty" question again. He still didn't answer the question directly, but recollected his youth, when the Taliban had ruled Kabul. He said he had very bad memories from those days. Without prompting, he talked about the forceful woman who had grilled General Kinkel with a five-minute speech followed by a half dozen questions.

"The woman sitting beside me in the meeting, she could never work when the Taliban were here," Najib said. "Now, she is my colleague." He struggled with the word *colleague* in English, but eventually pushed it out.

"What about you?" I asked. "Do you think international forces are here to help, or just make things worse? My daughter thinks we've done more harm than good."

"No, I do not believe that. Yes, there have been many mistakes made, and problems, but this is the best opportunity of my whole life."

That's what I was hoping you would say, I thought. But I knew my beautiful, brilliant daughter—who would have the PhD someday to prove it—would never buy my story when I got around to telling her about this day.

CHAPTER SEVEN

GENERAL ALLEN'S COMMAND came to an end in February, and another Marine four-star, Fighting Joe Dunford, took command of all American and NATO troops in Afghanistan. The change-of-command ceremony became heavier with four-star US Marines when General Jim Mattis joined the fray. Late in the day, I found myself in the Milano standing beside General Mattis. Someone snapped a photo and later sent it to me. In the photo, I'm talking and General Mattis is listening and laughing. I forgot pretty quickly about the specifics of the conversation, but wondered what I could've said to induce an outburst of laughter from the commander of US Central Command, one of the most significant combat commanders in the world.

General Dunford struck an immediate contrast with General Allen, engaging a group of top tier media just a few days after the change of command. I had seen a lot of leaders address the media, but Dunford was polished. Once he offered to answer a question "off the record," and the seasoned and reputable journalists had closed their notebooks and turned off their recording devices and stored them in backpacks and purses. General Dunford had answered the question and when he specified that the engagement was now back "on the record," the reporters started writing and recording again.

General Dunford and much of the leadership traveled to SHAPE headquarters in Belgium a few days later and Colonel Daniels sent Charlie Church along as a press adviser. I was a little jealous, but happy that Charlie was being rewarded for his outstanding work. When he returned a few days later, he only had hours, not days, to pack his bags and prepare for the journey home. He had served well, and his clear head and youthful enthusiasm had been an asset to our team.

Charlie Church went home in early March after a year in Afghanistan. It was almost like saying goodbye to one of my sons. My youngest son was in college at BYU. My oldest son was in medical school in Iowa. Charlie, who was the same age as my oldest daughter, was on his way home to his wife in Germany. He had been a superstar press officer, and I was not too proud to say Charlie Church had taught me a lot, and wisely, I had tried to listen to his advice and emulate his methods. He had recently given some advice to two contractors who had gotten stupid on us and ignored his advice. A few days later they lost their jobs and were sent home. I listened to him. I didn't care if he was thirty years old and could still be considered a rookie in the business. He was a natural, and when he offered advice, I gladly accepted and tried to act on it.

Colonel Daniels and I walked with him to the parking lot and threw his gear into a vehicle. It was cold and rainy. Watching him drive away was bittersweet. He deserved to be going home, but HQ ISAF would not be as strong without him. The compound was just a better place to live with Charlie Church in residence. Back in the office, I noticed an envelope under my keyboard. It said *Bristow* on the outside. I pulled out what felt like five or six sheets of printer paper, sat down, and started to read. It started with a brief, handwritten note, followed by a long, typed narrative.

Bristow, it's been an honor to serve with you. Since I know that you'll write a book someday, and that you'll ask me to write the foreword, I went ahead and drafted something in advance. Until we meet again, my friend—Charlie.

Your War
Foreword by Charlie Church
    Everyone's first day in theater is a scene they will never

let go of, for the rest of their days. For Bristow Watson, and for me, our first day was in Kabul—his a few years before me, but eventually the two of us shared time together there in 2012. This was at the heart of the war when we all still held hope and aspiration. All wars must end with desperation on both sides, and in retrospect I think our folly was that we weren't desperate yet. Perhaps we have never gotten desperate. Afghanistan during the surge was Bristow Watson's war, and it was my war too.

For everyone, the first day unrolls in painful slow motion, each moment branding itself into your head. For those cursed few that carry the holy dedication to being a writer, the details pile up in such vivid quantity that you shed tears trying to document this richness.

The first experience plays like a movie somebody choreographed, scripted, and filmed just for you. This is a place you never dreamed you would see, let alone breathe its air and taste its dust. But it's all real now and happening before you in fearful reality. Acrid diesel smoke and the stench of rotting vegetables overwhelm your lungs. The sounds of two-stroke engines, wailing muezzins, and bleating goats melt together into a metallic syrup that drips through your ears and pools in your sinus cavity. A boy no older than twelve uses a length of rebar to drive welts into the hindquarters of a skeletal donkey as the pathetic beast toils, pulling a cart piled high with handmade bricks.

A feeling of rabid enthusiasm washes over you and grabs one end of a rope in your brain, ready to get to work on something that finally feels like it matters. At the other end, tugging wildly, is a panicked regret. These two emotions pull in opposition to each other for the better part of your waking life for the next year; only a year, if you are lucky.

The attraction and absolute foolishness of the overall

war experience is that this complex memory—the moments of wide-eyed wonder, the discomfort and boredom, the grotesque inhumanity, the personal growth and the shame, the futility and the accomplishment—it's all just yours.

This ownership of a memory is so powerful, and so inspiring. But consider that as Bristow and I did our best in 2012, there were over one hundred thousand other wayward sinners from the United States, Europe, Australia, and dozens of other countries living their own period of brutality and beauty, working themselves to the bone, fighting, bleeding, dying, and for nearly everyone, living to return home and bury the memory of that time in the past. When we were all trying to achieve a supposedly shared goal, how do all of these experiences fuse together without standing alone?

It's shockingly easy to slide into bitter solitude and resentment. Your war stories start out good-natured, morbidly funny, even. But you somehow cross a Rubicon whenever you unlock this vault and start to page through the days you spent in theater. You get worked-up and somehow, unplanned, you get angry at a reason you can't understand, and those listening to your war stories politely nod and walk away, and you're only left to shake your fist at the sun— Nobody saw the true face of God the way that you did. If every soldier and every American voter and every piss-poor Afghan onion farmer and warlord and opium mule could just understand things as deeply and richly as you did, none of this would be necessary. You get it, why don't they? Why doesn't anybody? This simple answer is sitting right in front of our face, why can't we all just mutually agree to grasp it and bring peace to this horrible world?

Lonely memories always end up this way. The only way I have found to avoid sailing over this ledge is to learn how your singular time overlapped with just one other person's experience. If you're lucky, you'll find one intersection. If you open your heart and keep digging, the very humblest of us will see that your war was in many ways just like my war.

And while our war is a long way toward togetherness, we lose sight of the concept that the concept of us necessitates a them, some purpose and direction for all of this compounded rage.

And that is Bristow Watson's gift to us in the pages that follow. Everyone has war stories, but Bristow will find a way to silence all of the pointless noise, to find a thread among the sea of wool yarn ready for spinning, and bring us into his war, making it our war.

In these pages are the way Kabul is today, not like it was during those early Kite Runner days. For the last year my nostrils have burned with the alchemy of sizzling kabobs, helicopter exhaust, and burning trash that permeates Kabul. But with Brist Watson continuing to walk us through that world, I won't need to go back. Now we all can cling to a memory that made sense at one time. Perhaps it still does.

Whether you planned for it or not, this is now your war too.

Charlie Church
Kabul, Afghanistan
March 2013

Even after reading those passionately written words, and marveling how he described the immediate past, the present, and perhaps even his vision of Afghanistan's future, I still missed him, and was gloomy, like the weather, for the next few days. But just when the early-deployment loneliness crept back in, an old friend showed up at the headquarters, and unlike me, she had likely been elated to see the president reelected. We had been together the first time Barrack Obama was elected president, and I thought that maybe she had come back to taunt me. We had met four years ago in the first week of my first deployment here when I attended that NATO Strategic Communications seminar at the Kabul Serena Hotel. We had sat together through two days of meaningless strategy sessions led by Washington-based consultants who didn't know what it was like on the ground in Afghanistan. When I saw her the first time, at a kick-off breakfast, I thought she looked distinguished and confident. We hit it off immediately. She helped me pick out an expensive silk scarf for my wife's birthday. I found out later in my deployment that you could buy five or six scarves for what I had spent on the one Monika Winters picked out at the Hotel Serena gift shop. That had been more than four years ago, and now—I had never expected to see her again—she was back. I had not expected or anticipated her arrival, but she also didn't know I was at HQ ISAF, so that first encounter was interesting and a little embarrassing. Later, we recalled how easily and comfortably we had become friends at that fancy breakfast, in a fancy hotel, when those early days of my first deployment had erroneously created dream-like expectations that my entire first deployment would be fancy lunches at luxury hotels with attractive women and high-paid consultants. On that first morning, I had loaded up my plate at the succulent buffet and started looking for a place to sit among strangers. The seat beside the striking Monika Winters was available, and a close professional and personal relationship had begun. And now, here she was again, standing in front of the Yellow Building, the new spokesperson for the NATO senior civilian representative, her dream job. I saw her first and stood back as she was introduced to some of her new colleagues. Then she saw me, and struggled to maintain her bearing as NATO hotshots spoke to her as I distracted her by waving playfully from thirty feet away.

On her first night back in Kabul, we sat outside the Milano, in the same chairs we had sat in four years earlier, drank tea, and looked back.

"My god, it seems like we were just here," she said.

"That's how it feels to me. My two deployments here run together. Sometimes when I think about events in the past here, I have to stop and separate four years ago from four months ago. It's weird."

"John Coppard died," she said abruptly.

"Yeah, I read about it. I was surprised to hear that, but then I wasn't, because I remember him always being sick at the end of my first deployment. Who knew he had a gigantic brain tumor?"

"Yep. This was his dream job, and he didn't get to finish his tour here."

"Now it's your dream job."

"Yeah, I guess so," she said, holding back.

"On my first deployment here, the only time I didn't wear my uniform was on Christmas," I said. "I went with John to visit some of his NGO friends in the city. Looking back, I think it was both foolish and careless."

"Probably," she deadpanned.

I had driven back alone with his driver while he stayed at the party. That was crazy.

December 25, 2008
Kabul, Afghanistan

I stood near the main gate on Christmas Day and waited for John Coppard and his handler. I wore civilian clothes for the first time on my deployment. Finally, John and his driver showed up, and I broke every rule in the book, climbing into the back of a taxi with an Afghan driver. No armor. No long guns. No US Marines. Just unarmed John, an Afghan driver I didn't know, and my nine-millimeter with one extra clip. We showed up at the house of an American contractor who was getting paid handsomely to try and teach Afghan women how to knock down the barriers between them and the workforce.

"Great Brist, you brought your gun," she said sarcastically. So I placed it between the mattresses of a bed in the guest house. Good thing I didn't need it while I was there, because I would've never gotten to it fast enough. And since I would've been the only one armed, we would've all died anyway if the Taliban had overpowered the guards outside the compound and crashed the gate.

I foolishly rode back to the compound with that same driver, but without John Coppard, who chose to stay back and party with his friends.

It didn't take me long to realize how reckless and dangerous I had been on that Christmas Day in 2008. I had learned much more about insider attacks during my Dover experience. The only time I didn't wear my uniform or PT gear on the second deployment was when Monika came back from a three-day trip to Kandahar and called me at 10 p.m. to let me know she was back. I was already in the bed, but she convinced me to come sit with her at the Danish café, so I pulled on some sweatpants and trudged to the Danish café, sat with her while she drank coffee and told me about her trip. My attention was split between her and the gnawing fear that Colonel Jack Daniels or General Twitty would show up at the Danish café for a late-night snack.

The fight continued every day. On the battlefield, ISAF troops dominated. Every night American and ISAF special forces, in support of the Afghan National Army, snatched bad guys from their compounds, killed Taliban commanders and leaders, and took insurgents off the battlefield. But still, the Taliban figured out ways to kill American troops, and British troops, and occasionally the Georgians, who had become the biggest non-NATO contributor to the coalition. When the terrorists couldn't get to American and coalition troops, they kept killing civilians. When I was quoted as an ISAF spokesman, it was almost always to correct and often denounce the Taliban claims that their suicide bombers had killed dozens of ISAF troops, breached our perimeters, and captured our bases. We drafted news releases and opinion pieces in the voice of Afghan government leaders to denounce the insurgents, because the Afghan leaders themselves didn't do it enough. The insurgents' singular goal was to destabilize the government. They didn't need to win on the battlefield. They engaged and ran for cover. They hid in the villages. They built roadside bombs, paid poor, hungry Afghan men and boys food money—survival money—to plant IEDs and paid Afghan soldiers who could be bought to turn their weapons on coalition forces. Every American and coalition soldier they killed or injured was a victory, even if the insurgents sacrificed ten of their own for that one American casualty. On paper, the good guys were winning. But on the ground in Afghanistan, it was hard to feel that way. And back home, very few Americans understood or cared about battlefield victories or kinetic operations. Back home, wives and mothers, husbands and fathers, didn't know and understand that. All they knew was their sons, daughters, husbands, brothers, were coming home in aluminum cases draped by superbly starched, wrinkle-free American flags. I had seen that more than one hundred times on the ramp at Dover Air Force Base, where the bodies of dead American service members were treated with the greatest respect, and families were showered with care and support. But that didn't make the loss less painful, nor did it make the blood spilled less precious. And it sure as hell didn't make it easier to provide answers to people like Laura McGower and her broken-hearted daughter. Monika Winters still thought we could win, but not by fighting the way we were fighting. "We have to get concurrence from the Afghan people," she argued one night over tea. She loved that word *concurrence*. It was a really great word to use in a sentence, much harder to achieve. Monika and my American leadership clashed everyday about whose boss was more important, but when the duty day was over, Monika and I met every evening in the garden to rehash the day and try to make sense out of what had happened in the past twenty-four or forty-eight hours. We disagreed on almost everything—politically, philosophically—and yet we were inseparable. "I told you four years ago, if you want to reach the Afghan people, you have to engage the Afghan media."

"We do that every week with the press conference," I argued.

"We just feed them a bunch of prepared lines. We don't get them out among our troops to see what we're doing."

"Yeah, well that can be a little dangerous."

"I know. It's a fucking war. It's dangerous," she swore.

But her persistence and in-my-face attitude is how I had ended up in the Uzbin Valley with the French troops and their ANA counterparts four years earlier. I owed to her the memory of one of the most unique experiences of my first deployment, several days in the remote Uzbin Valley, a place you can't find on a map. But you can google it, and if you do, what will come up is the *Uzbin Valley Ambush*, a catastrophic and deadly event I had read about only hours before venturing into the Uzbin Valley myself, where in the hull of a French military armored personnel carrier, I had passed within a few kilometers of the location where French soldiers had been ambushed.

"You left so soon in 2009 that you never finished telling me about your trip to Uzbin Valley with the Afghan journalists," she said randomly.

So, I recollected to her the whole three days again.

April 29, 2009
Kabul

During the past few weeks I had begun to feel anxious to go home and anxious about going home—had I done all I could here? Are there things I wish I had done better or differently? Are there experiences I wanted to have but had not had? On those questions there would never be complete satisfaction. But I think on a three-day trip to Uzbin Valley some of that anxiety was eased. Before going I just felt like I wanted to get out of Kabul one more time before going home, and this trip gave me that, and it was all set up by Monika Winters, who chided me about the way the American public affairs team mishandled the Afghan media. Okay, then. Let's try to do better. The journey started at the French camp known by the creative title of Camp Warehouse, where we arrived at 9 p.m. and slept for a few hours in a tent. I was accompanied by Melissa (Mel) Preen from NATO TV, Hameed Rahim from Shamshad TV, Abaseen Zaheer from Shamshad TV, and MC1 Terry Matlock, USN, MPPAT photographer. We slept about fifty meters from a crater where a bomb had struck just a few nights earlier.

April 30, 2009
Camp Warehouse, Kabul

We got up at 2 a.m. and walked to the designated meeting point. There we were met by Lt. Eric Dardillac of the French Army, whom we immediately nicknamed Ricky Cadillac. We piled into French armored personnel carriers and rode the first hour in total darkness and silence. It was too loud to really carry on a conversation, although Mel tried. I just rested and contemplated the next few days, tried not to think about possible dangers lurking outside. After nearly an hour, the convoy came to a halt, and we opened the forward hatch above us and looked out into the early morning. We were in Jalalabad Pass. Straight above us were giant vertical cliffs that seemed to reach the sky. They looked like large looming shadows right over us. I only looked out the hatch for a moment and then sat back inside the armored personnel

carrier. We moved slowly through the pass and then were on
the open road again. I had no idea at the time how new and
smooth the road was until I saw it in daylight on the return trip
three days later. From Surobi to Kabul the road is new and
firmly paved. We passed Surobi and then it was dirt roads and
narrow mountain passes all the way to Combat Outpost Dabo
(COP Dabo . . . I thought of Clemson football coach Dabo
Swinney). We maneuvered a few kilometers north and west
of Sper Kuber, a village in the Uzbin Valley where French,
American, and Afghan troops had been ambushed by the
Taliban eight months earlier. The ten French casualties were
the most combat deaths for France in more than twenty-five
years. I should've been more concerned, knowing about the
raid. But, I was confident in our security posture, probably
because I didn't know any better. Later when the sun had
risen above the mountains that encircled us—and I hoped
that would be the only walls that surrounded us—and we
were moving up the Uzbin Valley, I climbed into the hatch
again and rode there for miles, enthralled by the magnificent
landscape. Why were so many people fighting over this
enchanted land? The convoy maneuvered up narrow roads,
right on the edge of steep cliffs and drop-offs. The drivers
were good. We arrived at COP Dabo at 7 a.m. It seemed
like much later. Ahead of me were sixty hours I would never
forget, and the experience I needed to feel like I could finally
go home.

Command Outpost Dabo
Uzbin Valley, Afghanistan

A few minutes after reaching COP Dabo I spoke to a
US Marine major because I wanted to get some background
on the ANA mentoring role American and French troops
were engaged in here. He took me to meet Colonel Langley,

USMC (and Wesley Snipes look-alike). I recognized him immediately as the same USMC colonel I had seen and met briefly at BWI last October, even though he had been in civilian clothes. We actually flew from Baltimore to Manas on the same plane. Colonel Langley commanded all the US mentor teams in eastern Afghanistan. I was impressed by him presently just I had been during that first encounter. Our journalists did a few interviews and we rested in our suite (tent) for a few minutes before the shura—which is a meeting of the local village elders and Afghan and coalition military leaders. The men from all the local villages began arriving at least an hour early. They sat against a building fifty meters in the distance, gathered in various other small groups, and waited to be summoned. Finally, the different village leaders came to the shura center and had a discussion. Then thirty minutes later the rest of the men and boys began to come to the shura center. At first it looked like only twenty or thirty men and boys (no girls allowed, of course), but they just kept coming until there were eventually close to one hundred people attending. I took a lot of pictures of the men and boys, especially the young boys—the future of Uzbin Valley.

After the Afghan interpreter "Harley" welcomed everyone, an ANA officer sang or chanted some kind of prayer or anthem. Then the speakers took the floor, one at a time. One of the boys kept motioning for me to give him my pen. But that was the one thing I had to keep, because I knew I would be taking a lot of notes. Interestingly enough, I later helped him carry bags of flour and rice outside of the wire after the ANA performed a humanitarian relief mission of commodities. When I was helping him carry his wheat, he talked to me in his language and the desperation in his voice and his body language were heart-wrenching. What was he saying? What did he need? I wished we could've had a long conversation. It would have been fascinating to hear about his life. In addition to the one hundred or so people who showed up for the shura, another thirty to forty ANA, ANP, French, and US military officers and soldiers observed or stood guard. Mel Preen was the only woman allowed at the shura, although we could see women and girls observing from afar, at least a hundred meters removed from the men. During the shura I wrote in my notes: "After the Ariana TV visit yesterday and this developing experience, I can go home feeling enriched by the six-month experience. This country is worth fighting for." I know I felt that, but did I believe it? And why did I believe it? While one of the first speakers was making his pitch, the ANA started handing out water bottles to everyone, which interrupted the speech. So the man just waited for the water distribution. It was near noon now and the sun was starting to bear down hard.

At the end of the shura, one of the old local men got up and gave a lively monologue about something. He got very animated. I asked Abaseen Zaheer what the man was saying and Abaseen explained something about the man's grandson being picked up by the ANP for firing a rocket at Afghan forces. Not exactly egging passing cars on Veterans Road in Columbia, something for which my son had been picked up once. But, the old man pleaded, his grandson was a good boy and innocent of wrong-doing. I hoped he was innocent, because I couldn't imagine what the ANP officers would do to him if the accusations were true. The shura lasted about an hour and a half. Right at the end, the ANA general from Kabul showed up (he was the cause of the seventy-five-minute delay to start with) and held an "executive" session with a half dozen local leaders while the ANA gave out the humanitarian relief supplies. I watched the humanitarian relief mission take place and really felt sorry for the people.

The little boys were carrying heavy bags of flour and rice, plus uninflated soccer balls and other goodies. They all tried to carry too much. I helped several of the boys get their stuff outside the wire. Once outside the ANA cordon, they seemed very relieved. I know it must've taken hours for some of those people to get that stuff home. All the boys and men set out walking in different directions. Some would walk for miles, loaded down with their supplies. We went to a few of the villages the next day, so I know how far they were. The next day I even saw one of the boys I recognized from the shura, and he was walking on the road at least three kilometers from COP Dabo. After the shura, I ate lunch with the ANA—rice, naan, lamb, and broth to dip the naan in. Delicious! Later I played volleyball with some ANA soldiers. Some of them were quite good, as volleyball is very popular here. I ate dinner with them also, which was just naan dipped in the sauce—no rice or lamb. They eat light for dinner. Don't see too many overweight Afghans. I never gave a thought to being in danger when I foolishly allowed myself to be alone with the ANA soldiers. Green-on-Blue attacks were not as common in 2009 as they would become a few years later. However, I was as apprehensive about venturing outside the walls of the compound to relieve myself in the latrine trench, where I squatted to do my business and looked out toward a slope, wondering if a couple of Taliban fighters might charge over that hill and catch me with my pants down—literally. Luckily, that didn't happen.

May 1, 2009
Uzbin Valley, Afghanistan

Early today we set out on a foot patrol with French soldiers. They wanted to check out some holes in the cave near a local village to make sure it wasn't a hideout for IED-making materials. I rode in the hatch from COP Dabo to the village. The landscape was magnificent! We disembarked from the vehicles, observed the village from afar for a few minutes then started on the foot patrol. The first thing we walked past were beautiful, colorful poppy fields, which would look magnificent in a painting, but in reality, would eventually turn in to heroin. They were inter-mingled among wheat fields, but it's hard to hide those bright pink and white flowers. When we started out there were a lot of locals meandering around on the perimeter of the village, but once we started their way all the women and children seemed to disappear into the village and just the men stayed out in the relative open. Around one bend we came across children, sitting in an open field, tending their sheep. We worked our way down into a riverbed, crossed a small creek and then around the perimeter of the village on a narrow, hillside footpath. We were careful not to damage a rock wall that we crossed, didn't disturb the poppy field and especially not the wheat. Maybe if the ANA had been with us, they might've trampled on the poppies just for good measure. After an hour we returned to our patrol base and waited for another half hour while the French soldiers patrolled a nearby area and freed one of their vehicles that had run off the edge of the road and gotten stuck. I took some photos of shepherd boys herding their sheep and goats from one hillside to another. They approached me, undeterred, and I gave them several large water bottles. I talked in English, they spoke in their native tongue, and we both smiled and laughed like we actually understood each other. Maybe we did. One of the patrols on our far flank reported seeing ten suspected armed insurgents on the move in the hills to our North. I thought we were heading back to the base, but we actually bypassed COP Dabo and took up a rear position with the patrol pursuing the bad guys. We advanced five hundred meters and then sat for an hour while the French squad on foot pursued in the hills above us. We called in an unmanned aerial vehicle (UAV), and it flew overhead for about an hour, reporting back its findings—movement of at least one armed man in the area just north of us, so we stayed in pursuit. We kept up this maneuver—move five hundred meters and watch the hills for an hour—for several hours. We stayed in pursuit the rest of the morning and into the afternoon, eventually pushing five kilometers up the valley. We never encountered any insurgents, which was probably good for them because we had about ten heavily armed vehicles and thirty to forty heavily armed French infantry, probably still angry about the ambush on their brothers less than a year earlier—so we could've brought some pretty good firepower to bear had we needed to. About an hour into this second leg of our patrol, the Afghan journalists grew bored, said they had enough film for their report, and wanted to walk back to COP Dabo, which was five hundred meters or more behind us. Morons! I should've let them walk back. But when I reminded them that only the ANA were at the COP, they changed their minds quickly, and I realized something I had perceived the day before—that our boys from the city were actually afraid of the ANA soldiers and preferred to stay close to the French and Americans. At one point we came to a twenty-foot square area surround by a stone wall. On the perimeter a white flag flew from a tall pole made of a delimbed tree. A white flag in my mind means someone is trying to surrender. A white flag in this culture (or at least in Kandahar) means the area is occupied by Taliban. When we came to the white flag our Afghan reporters got excited and started working again. When our convoy halted near the square plot of ground Terry, Mel, and I went to investigate.

There was a lot of debate about what the white flag meant. We walked across a creek and found that it was a small cemetery—not sure if it was Taliban graves or just common Afghans. At this stop I also ate my first French MRE. It was better than an American MRE and I ended up eating two more French MREs before this excursion was over.

We kept pushing up the valley, eventually four or five kilometers north of COP Dabo. We had begun this patrol at 6:30 a.m. and at 3 p.m. we took our last position to cover the return of the French soldiers on foot who had walked the entire ridge line above us as we made our way up the valley in vehicles. The soldiers eventually came down the hill at 4 p.m. and we collected the weary lads, loaded up the vehicles, and started the slow, bumpy return to the camp. I wondered if the French soldiers would be disappointed that there wasn't a fight since we were in the general area where ten French soldiers had died in the ambush last August. I asked Ricky Cadillac if they would be disappointed, and he said they were not because had they engaged the Taliban there would have been a chance for someone to be killed or wounded and they preferred to avoid that risk. They probably would've liked to avenge the death of their ten brothers, but Ricky said even if they killed every Taliban in the valley, it would not bring back their brothers. Well said, Lt. Eric Dardillac. Americans probably would've felt differently. I think Americans would've come back to the camp pissed off that they didn't have a firefight. While we were waiting for the soldiers to come down from the hills, I sat atop our APC and wrote these notes in my journal and wondered again how I would ever accurately describe this day to my family. Luckily, I have lots of pictures and some shaky, grainy video to help illustrate what this day was like. Terry Matlock took hundreds of photos too, and actually got some good shots of me, which I appreciate very much. As I sat on the APC writing, I looked out over this magnificent valley where we were chasing Taliban and thought that if the insurgents would just leave this valley, we could leave this valley and the simple and innocent people of Uzbin Valley could get on with their lives—which I believe is what they would want. They want that, we want that, and now we need the bad guys to allow that. Terry said I could explain the day like this: "move a kilometer, sit for an hour; move a kilometer, sit for an hour." That was our day, but it was still one of the most memorable days of my deployment. It's not every day that you run with French infantry, chat up Afghan shepherd boys, chase the Taliban, sit atop an armored personnel carrier, and try to describe with words what you had seen and done for your journal, or what might become your moving memoir or renowned novel.

May 2, 2009
Uzbin Valley, Afghanistan

The next morning, we started for home. But someone, maybe Colonel Langley, called in a mission. We stopped on a hillside and joined up with a company of ANA soldiers for the purpose of responding to intelligence that bomb-making materials may be stored in a local village. The French commander insisted that Mel, the Afghan journalists, and I stay back in the base camp with Ricky Cadillac. We did send Terry Matlock with the patrol. We sat on a hillside and watched the patrol through high-powered binoculars. The team did not discover a huge cache of weapons but did find artillery shells and other ammunition. The French engineers attached explosives to the stash and blew it up. We saw the smoke from several miles away, and a few seconds later heard the muffled explosion. Mission accomplished.

The team was away from the main camp for at least three hours, so I found another one of those French MREs, found a shady spot opposite the sunny side of an armored personnel carrier and popped open my lunch. It had one of the flammable gel cannisters like the apparatus we used on scout campouts to heat our food. I actually had a hot meal sitting in the middle of an Afghanistan field while a combat patrol completed a weapons disposal mission.

On the trip home we navigated the Jalabad pass in daylight, and I saw more clearly the steep, dramatic cliff faces. We tossed food and candy to Afghan children chasing our convoy. The commander quickly ordered that to cease after a few kids wandered precariously close to our fast-moving vehicles. Afghan teenagers splashed carefree in the Kabul River between Surobi and Kabul. At Camp Warehouse, when Sergeants Mack and Fleming came to pick me up, I bought them dinner in a Turkish Restaurant. It was time to go home.

Monika was right. I had left rather abruptly in 2009. Those three days in the Uzbin Valley were really my last memories from that deployment. Getting home was a frustrating five-day ordeal. The day after I arrived home, I got on the internet to read the latest Afghanistan news and email the colleagues I left behind to let them know that I already missed them. Colonel Daniels called me into his office in early March and told me to close the door. The last time this had happened, he told me he hated the Afghan people and there was no chance for us to be successful. He was pissed about the election too. I wasn't pissed at the election. I was devastated. I thought Romney could rescue the country. The closed-door meeting four months ago had triggered a frightening anxiety attack. I wondered what kind of surprise he had for me this time.

"I told Pete Bryant I would find him a spot in the MOC if he would do the exec. job for another month, so I need to make good on that," he said.

"Sure, we can work together."

"I want to make him chief of the media operations center," he said. I wondered if he noticed my furrowed brow. Was I being fired?

"It's no reflection on your performance; I just want to give him a chance to lead. I know you're about to retire, so why don't you go home a month early. I'd be glad to release you."

I knew he didn't understand the Reserve retirement system, so I summarized it in a half dozen quick statements—that I needed to complete six months to get the various benefits triggered by serving in a combat zone in ninety-day increments. So, he said we would figure something out, but he wanted to make the change on April 1, at my five-month point. No, this was not an April Fool's joke.

As luck would have it, my friend Bryan Thomas, embedded with special operators at KAIA, did understand the Reservist retirement system, or maybe he just understood people better than Jack Daniels, the deeply engrained human need to finish something you started. I didn't volunteer for a five-month deployment. So when I explained my predicament to Bryan Thomas, a mutually beneficial opportunity fell into both of our laps with the Joint Special Operations Task Force.

"I'm about to go on leave," he said. "Come up here and fill in for me while I'm gone. That'll guarantee you another two or three weeks, and Jack can move the major into your spot right now. Sounds like he wants to take care of the active-duty guys."

"Yeah, I think so. They need to beef up their résumés, not me. I get it."

Colonel Daniels signed off on the idea and a week later, I relocated to KAIA to spend five days with Bryan before he departed on leave. I enjoyed the crash course in special operations public affairs. Living quarters were so tight on KAIA that I just moved in with Bryan and slept on the floor in his room, then just threw some fresh sheets on the bed after he left. It was interesting to "live" at KAIA North. At the end of my first deployment, construction had moved ahead at fever pitch, and I participated in the public affairs planning for the "grand opening" of the compound. Everything back then had been fresh and new. Now, four years later, those same facilities were hammered from heavy use and abuse from the everyday austere conditions of Kabul summers and winters.

One night before Bryan's departure, he escorted me to the Special Ops tactical operations center so we could view a mission in progress. The objective was to free an American doctor being held hostage by the Taliban. The special operators would infiltrate the area by helicopter, charge across the dark ground for five kilometers in the middle of the night and assault the compound where the doctor was being held, if the intel was correct. I had seen this type of operation portrayed on television and in the movies, and it went down almost exactly the same way. Except when two Navy SEALs actually took on enemy fire, they were gravely wounded, and actors were never gravely wounded in the movies. Unlike in the movies, when opposing forces fill the air with thousands of rounds of ammunition, it's impossible to run right through that fray without getting hit. Someone gets hit by a ricochet or something. The rescue of Dr. Dilip Joseph cost the life of a Navy SEAL Nicolas Checque, who was twenty-eight years old, and gave me a more detailed look at special forces than I ever thought I'd observe in person or would ever want again. A few years later when Navy SEAL Edward Byers was awarded the Medal of Honor for the operation, it was hard to believe that I had actually been there, sort of. I had been a nervous and fascinated observer.

A few nights later, American and Afghan special forces captured three Taliban bombmakers in Kunar province. Our soldiers moved the civilians to a safe location and then called in an air strike on the Taliban compound to kill the rest of the insurgents. When the SOF operators pulled out, other insurgents in the area leveled the village with RPGs, killing all the villagers—men, women, and children—that American and Afghan forces had risked their own lives to protect.

Then the insurgents called leaders from a nearby village to inspect the carnage and destruction. Afghan media were called in and it was reported that Americans had killed dozens of innocent Afghans. I learned the harsh realities of false allegations and fabricated propaganda, and how effectively the enemy deployed them. I was glad when Bryan Thomas returned from leave. I caught a convoy back to HQ ISAF to starting packing for my own redeployment.

CHAPTER EIGHT

WITH A WEEK remaining until my departure for home, Colonel Jack Daniels had another last mission for me. I wasn't sure I wanted another last mission, but when he told me the nature of the assignment—to escort a well-connected journalist to Khost for an important story she was working on for *American Stories* magazine— it sounded better than sitting around the camp watching the clock for my last two days. It had a strange, but familiar ring to it, like Monika sending me to Uzbin Valley with the Afghan journalists in 2009. Except this time, Monika was nowhere to be found. She had departed on leave while I was at KAIA with the SOF.

The embed was approved above the general officer level, I was told. Operators were attached to the mission, a security detail, helicopters and dedicated Humvees. Laura Paige Hatfield was getting the red-carpet treatment. So, I googled her, and everything I found on her was twenty years old, when she had been a feature writer for *Newsweek*. Hmmm. Was this her comeback tour?

Sergeants Mackay and Shealy, my drivers and security detail, were neither impressed nor thrilled when I told them about the mission, especially because we had to go out at seven in the evening to pick up Laura Paige Hatfield at the Serena Hotel and bring her back to HQ ISAF so we could catch a Blackhawk flight the next morning. We geared up, reviewed the security briefings, and departed HQ ISAF just after six. The traffic was horrendous! Mackay and Shealy swore a lot, sometimes under their breath, sometimes at Afghan drivers, sometimes at pedestrians who walked in and out of traffic. They probably wanted to drop a few f-bombs on me but knew they couldn't get away with that.

Jammed between an assortment of vehicles in the Massoud roundabout, I thought about those warnings—be on the lookout for any number of suspicious white Toyota Corollas believed to be in the hands of insurgents for the purpose of carrying out attacks against NATO forces. But every third vehicle on Kabul's streets was a white Toyota Corolla, and another third were Toyota minivans that looked like they had been driven a million miles on European streets and then shipped to Kabul for additional duty. The minivans were always packed beyond belief with people, so those didn't concern us as much. Insurgents liked to use one suicide bomber at a time, not a carload for one mission. That would've been a drain on their resources. Sergeant Mackay was not in the mood to share the road or demonstrate any of the courteous driving practices we had been ordered to use, so we had several near collisions between the headquarters and the Serena.

My transport and security team arrived outside the walls of the Serena just before eight. I egressed the vehicle, against the advice of my driver and gunner. Shealy tried to beat me out of the vehicle.

"Stay in the vehicle, Shealy. If there are going to be any risks, I'll take them," I told him.

"Yes, sir," he said, and I knew that was difficult for him. Perhaps at this moment he hated getting ordered, because for months he had protected me, and I knew that was foremost on his mind. But I ordered him to stay in the car and keep watch this time, and he obeyed my order, thinking I'm sure that the risks had started the moment we drove through the HQ ISAF gate.

I walked straight to the dark-suit security officer standing in front of the thick, steel gate, spoke to him less than ten seconds, then returned to the vehicle. Almost instantly, the large, heavy gate began to separate. Sergeant Mackay eased the Land Cruiser past the gates, a half dozen armed guards, the guard boss who flicked a quick thumbs-up at me as we passed. The sergeant rolled the vehicle through the covered front entrance of the luxury hotel, positioned the Land Cruiser facing out, brought the vehicle to a stop but didn't cut the engine. I jumped out of the vehicle again, started for the hotel entrance, but she was quicker. The gigantic, sculpted door pushed open, and I met this renowned journalist—Laura Paige Hatfield—whom I had never before heard of in my life. She wanted to see the battlefield so she could write a book or series of feature stories to help American mothers know what their sons and daughters were dying for. The theme rang familiar in my head. She looked familiar.

She carried a heavy backpack like the ones my NCOs hauled into combat.

"Ms. Hatfield?"

"Laura Paige is fine," she said, extending her hand. She held onto the grip for an odd extra second and stared at me, then released the grip and the stare.

"I'm Brist Watson from the ISAF public affairs office."

"Nice to meet you. And thanks for coming to get me."

"Yes ma'am."

I think I caught her rolling her eyes when I called her 'ma'am.'

Sergeant Mackay opened the double-armored back doors, pulled out a body armor ensemble and traded Laura Paige Hatfield the body armor for the backpack. He gripped it with both hands like lifting a small child, tossed it into the Land Cruiser and slammed the doors shut. I sensed some hostility, made eye contact with him, and defused the tension with a quick wink. I was the "lieutenant colonel of all lieutenant colonels," a phrase Mackay had coined months earlier in a clumsy attempt to demonstrate respect after I returned the ten dollars to him I had won in a poker game.

"Is this necessary?" she asked, looking at the body armor and helmet.

"It's required," I said. "Without it, you can't ride in our vehicles, or on the ISAF helicopter, or embed with the units."

She picked up the heavy body armor and wrestled with it

awkwardly. I tried to untangle it as she clumsily strained to throw it over her shoulders and put her head through the opening. One of the steel plates smacked her in the back of the head. I flinched.

"That's happened to me a lot," I offered.

She eventually got the body armor over her head, and it dropped across her chest and back. I carefully retrieved the elastic waistband, handed her each end and she pulled it tightly around her. Then I snatched the front flap up to expose a flat, Velcro square in the front. I pulled the side plates into place, slapped each of the front straps to the Velcro and covered them with the front flap. Everything was in place and tightly fastened. I held the door and motioned her into the back seat of the vehicle, closed the door, and ran around to the other side. When I was sitting beside her in the backseat, I looked over at her. She looked like she was reaching for the seatbelt.

"You don't need that," I said.

"I always wear my seat belt."

"Me too. But not here. If something happens, you might need to egress the vehicle quickly."

She shrugged. I banged on the back of Mackay's seat, and he eased the vehicle forward.

"Put on your helmet," I said, not looking at her.

We exited the fortified Serena compound and moved back into the Kabul night. The streets were eerily empty, like everyone had arrived at their destinations in the past ten minutes. Darkness came quickly and covered the city like a heavy blanket. Electricity was spread sparsely throughout the city. Streetlamps were few and dim. The night was spooky.

"Wow, the city seems to have shut down," she shouted.

"Yep. It was crazy twenty minutes ago," I replied. "Did you eat dinner?" I asked her.

"I wasn't hungry."

"We're up at 0600 and on the choppers by seven, so not sure when we'll eat next. Do you want to eat breakfast before we leave?"

"Not really, but you can. I don't eat much," she said.

"You know, where we're going is a dangerous place. The insurgents attack the base all the time, and we've lost a lot of soldiers by suicide attacks in the city."

She had a strained look on her face, but not fear. Something else.

"I'm aware of that. I did my homework," she said, straight-faced. "If you're trying to scare me, it's not working. I know all too well that it's a combat zone."

How did she know? I wondered. I didn't see in her credentials that she had traveled or worked in Afghanistan previously.

"I'm not trying—"

She interrupted. "I didn't come here to stay in the Serena. I don't care where I have to pee, or how dangerous it is. I'm familiar with the area. I know it's dangerous. But I have a job to do."

Point taken. We arrived back at HQ ISAF, and I put Laura Paige Hatfield in temporary quarters for the night.

"I'll pick you up at seven," I said, and left her there.

When I showed up outside her hooch ten hours later with my backpack and gear, she was sitting on hers, anxious, impatient, determined. She looked different from the night before. There was something about her hair, and the makeup probably applied at the Serena was gone now. She looked ready, and I was impressed, though I didn't say so.

We walked in full battle rattle to the soccer field. No one was there. No Blackhawks were there. The morning was gray, not sure if it was overcast or just the heavy cloud of smoke that rested into this giant bowl-shaped city. It was usually midmorning before we could separate the clouds from the smoke.

"Hmmm," I sighed. I probably meant to do that silently, but it came out as a perplexed, questioning sound. "This is not what I expected."

"What time is the flight?"

"Seven-thirty," I replied. "To be honest, I'm not really sure what's going on, exactly. Monika Winters set this up. Just told me to pick you up, be here to catch a chopper to FOB Salerno. Then she decided to go on leave. Anyway, some generals are coming with us, I think."

"They'll be here, I'm sure," she said.

"Yeah. Might be running late. We just didn't get the memo."

But two minutes later, the calvary—so to speak—showed up. Four vehicles rolled up and stopped parallel to the perimeter wall of the soccer field. Close support teams jumped out, followed by a general and two colonels. The general walked straight to me but spoke to Laura Paige Hatfield.

"Ms. Hatfield?"

"That's right," she said, shaking his hand.

"I understand you're coming with us, to report on the progress of the campaign in Khost?"

"Yes sir," she said respectfully.

"Welcome. The colonel will take good care of you, I'm sure."

"He's doing a good job so far, General."

As if on cue, we heard in the distance the staccato beat of helicopters. The chopping grew louder and within seconds two UH-60 Blackhawks were over the soccer field. They descended one behind the other and landed fifty yards apart. The engines roared. I had not thought about ear protection.

The general and the colonels started toward the closest Blackhawk, followed by four close protection team members. I crowded in behind them but was redirected by a flight engineer who pointed me and Laura Paige Hatfield to the distant aircraft. Thankfully, my seatbelts were untangled and displayed across the seat so I could buckle quickly and appear to know what I was doing. When I was strapped in tight, I led Laura Paige through the process using awkward hand signals. She didn't seem to need my help and was buckled securely just a few seconds after me. The engineer handed us earplugs. It's a good thing someone was thinking for me. A minute later, we rose above the soccer field, then above the

Green Zone and HQ ISAF, and then above the city. Kabul in the early morning was a haunting and magnificent site, gray and brown and dimly lit, miles and miles of city and its people. On my left and right I saw signs of life, cars moving, new apartment buildings under construction, office buildings that looked almost like they would fit into an American city—a poor, rundown American city in a worn-out section of town. On the outskirts of the city we saw what looked like refugee camps, ghettos that stretched to the foot of the tall mountains that rimmed the eastern part of the city. Then the Blackhawks rose to clear the cliffs and Kabul was behind us.

The Blackhawks skimmed above the terrain like it was a contest to see which one could stay closest to the ground without hitting anything. Been there. Done that. Looking across at Ms. Hatfield, I recalled another day in my first Afghanistan deployment, the last time I had escorted journalists on a battlefield circulation, or an abbreviated embed. I remembered that frightening day flying across Herat and Farah Province in the Italian Chinooks four years earlier. Scariest day of my life!

A half hour into the flight, I saw the dark profile of a tall, east-to-west mountain range that hugged the Pakistan border. I remembered it from that large topographical map back at Bagram a few months earlier. The mountain range was backlit by the rising sun that beamed into the chopper and aimed a spotlight on Laura Paige Hatfield as she looked away from me. It became daylight without any fanfare as I stared at a profile I was growing more certain I had seen before. Then, with the sunrise encircling her face, she became like some kind of vision to me, and I knew exactly when and where I had seen her before—on a dark, cold night, two years earlier.

I leaned into her, pulling my seat restraint as far forward as it would allow, almost choking myself, and yelled above the shrill of the rotor blades turning right over our heads.

"How did you pull this off?"

She stared at me.

"You're Laura McGower, aren't you?"

"What?"

"Laura McGower! I knew I recognized you!"

"My name is Laura Paige Hatfield," she yelled back.

"Bullshit! You're the mom, with the daughter. At Dover. I was there," I yelled even louder. "Your son was . . ."

She just stared at me, pretending not to hear me, but then her expression changed, and pain came across her face. I kept yelling, and the flight engineer turned to see what all the commotion was.

"How in the hell? What are you doing here?" I screamed. She didn't have to answer that question either. She could claim not to hear clearly, or understand me, feigning the overbearing noise of the helicopter. But, then I knew instantly. Of course. Khost. We were on our way to Khost.

I sat back in my seat, and the firm straps that held me tight relaxed a little, and I wasn't choking anymore. I felt like I had just sprinted a few hundred meters and took some deep breaths. I stared at her, but she looked out the window like a tourist, a half smile working its way across her face. The next fifteen minutes passed slowly, and I didn't know whether to be angry or enthusiastic. I had thought about her many times since that black night at Dover. Now, for a moment a weight lifted off me. I no longer had to look for answers. She had journeyed here to find out for herself. Now, inside my own head, there was a pause, then a surge of anxiety came back as I wondered, *What if she doesn't find any answers*? Then her burden would be heavier than ever.

Right before the helicopter landed, I saw Khost city out my right window. It was a thriving city, but dangerous. It was close to the Pakistan border. It was strategic. But more than anything, precious blood had been spilled on its streets and sidewalks. When she saw the city, I knew exactly what she was thinking. Where did it happen?

The helicopter landed on a paved pad adjacent to Forward Operating Base Salerno, one of the oldest coalition bases in

Afghanistan. FOB Salerno had seen a lot of action. Its perimeters had been attacked over and over by Taliban fighters. It was a dangerous place to live and work. The engines unwound and the chopping sound turned to a high-pitched whine, until the generators were shut down and there was almost silence. A group of American officers walked toward our group. Most of them peeled off toward the general and colonels. Two young American soldiers, a female captain and a male sergeant, walked directly toward me and Laura Paige Hatfield, or whatever her name was. Our smiling, enthusiastic hosts were upon us before I could re-engage with Laura McGower.

"Welcome to FOB Salerno," the captain said.

"Thank you," Laura Paige said. She shook hands with the captain and introduced herself as Laura Paige Hatfield.

We started walking and the captain kept talking. The colonels and general got into vehicles and drove away with their entourage, which included all the security and support staff. By the time we got off the ramp there were no vehicles. The sergeant took Laura Paige's backpack, and tried to take mine, but I refused his offer and threw it across my back, struggling awkwardly to situate it behind my body armor.

"We've got some good things for you to see," the captain said. "As I understand it, your assignment is just to write stories about what progress has been made here and how the coalition forces have secured and stabilized this area so the Afghan forces can take over security."

"It's a little deeper than that," I said as we walked.

"Deeper, sir?"

"I think Ms. Hatfield's goal here is to find some distinct answers to the question, 'what are we doing here and are the sacrifices worth all the good people we've lost?'" I looked at Laura Paige and she stared me down. "Did I sum that up correctly, ma'am?" I asked her directly.

"Yes, Colonel Watson, I think you did," she said.

"Okay then," the captain said, less sure of herself now. "I hope we don't disappoint."

"If I'm disappointed, I'm certain it won't be due to your lack of good work and diligence," Laura said.

We crossed through a checkpoint and the captain showed her badge. Then we were between rows of tents and metal containers, which made up the majority of offices and living quarters. The captain and sergeant stopped us in front of a tent.

"We're very crowded here," she said apologetically. "I'm afraid we just have one tent for transients, so I hope you don't mind sharing." She opened the door to the heavy-duty tent and shrugged. "Life in the combat zone."

"It's fine," Laura said.

We walked into the dark tent, which was illuminated by a single light bulb hanging in the middle. There were ten cots on each side. It appeared around half were occupied. Laura Paige coaxed the sergeant into giving up her backpack, walked to the far-right corner, and dropped her backpack on the last cot. I followed, unsure if I should sleep beside her, or pick another cot on the other side that would give her some space.

"We'll give you a chance to ground your gear and rest for a few minutes," the captain said. "Latrines are right outside," she added, pointing to her left. "Fifteen minutes?"

"That'll be fine," I said, still holding my backpack.

The captain and sergeant retreated, so I approached Laura cautiously.

"Can I bunk here, or would you prefer some privacy?"

"Privacy, seriously? Right there is fine," she said, motioning with her head to the cot that was only four feet from the one she had chosen in the corner.

I unstrapped my body armor and dropped it at the foot of my cot. I unclipped my nine-millimeter and laid it carefully on the cot beside me. I had not cleared it and there was still a round in the chamber. She dropped to the cot right beside her backpack, still heavily encumbered by her body armor.

"You can take off your gear," I said.

"I'll keep in on for now, thanks."

I sat on the cot and removed the air-packed sleeping bag from my backpack, stood up and rolled the sleeping bag out on the cot. I pushed my pack to the foot-end of the cot, sat back down, leaned over, and buried my face in my hands. I wasn't sure what would happen next with Laura McGower now sitting on a cot beside me, almost close enough for her knees to knock against mine. I sat upright and looked straight at her. She was ready.

"This is some uncharted territory," I said.

"Meaning . . ."

"I'm not sure," I said. She waited, so I guessed it was my turn again. "How did you pull this off? How did you get here?"

"I'm really a journalist," she said.

"Twenty years ago. I googled you. Are you really on assignment? Are you going to write something?"

"I told my editor I might write a book . . . and I might. But that's not the main reason I'm here."

"And what is the main reason?"

"I know you haven't forgotten about my meeting with you on the ramp at Dover," she stated firmly.

"Nope."

"The journalist thing was the only way to get here, so I used it. But, I'm a mother first. That's why I'm here. I promised my daughter I would find out what her brother died for. You were there. You heard me promise her."

I stared at her. I had only been sure it was her for the past half hour or so. But she knew me the moment she saw me outside the Serena.

"It took me a while to recognize you, but seems you knew all along it was me. Did you know I was here?"

We only had ten minutes until the bright, young captain would return. So Laura gave me the abbreviated version. She knew Monika Winters, so that was her first contact. Monika mentioned I was head of media operations at ISAF.

"I told her your name sounded familiar to me," she said. "Apparently you had told her about your Dover experience, and then, of course, I remembered immediately. I googled you too."

I smiled and gave her an agreeable nod.

"Monika suggested I brush off my media credentials. I told her I wanted you to be my escort."

"Wow, and I just thought she approached me because she knew I wanted to get out of Kabul once last time before my deployment was over."

"Guess she knew that was part of it, but of course, she was honoring my request. She knows about my son, my family. She wanted to do something to help me."

"She knows about Dover, and the experience with your daughter on the ramp?" I asked.

"And my meeting with you that night. Yep, she knows about that now. Every detail of that night."

"Never said a word to me. She's a good friend of yours, that's for sure. And she can keep a secret."

Laura McGower, a.k.a. Laura Paige Hatfield. I wasn't sure what to call her, but thought I'd play it safe and make sure I use the pen name on her embed request. Laura Paige Hatfield smiled and gave me a gentle nod. I knew then we were going to be okay. She placed a device on the cot beside her.

"What's that?"

"Portable GPS."

"What are you planning to do with it?"

"I don't know. Just thought it might be useful."

Something troubled me, but I wasn't sure what.

"Be careful with it. I'd hate for someone to get their hands on it, and have our exact location marked."

"I won't lose it."

If I'd had some more intel training, I might've discerned better why it bothered me that she had brought with her a portable GPS. But I didn't have the technical expertise to make an intelligent argument about it.

The captain and sergeant appeared, approaching us carefully.

"Are you ready?" the captain asked.

"We're ready," Laura assured her.

"Don't you want to take off your gear, ma'am," the sergeant asked. "We're going to be on the FOB until after lunch. It's safe."

"Not according to the colonel here," Laura poked me. "He said this was the most rocketed FOB in the country and I was risking my life by coming here."

The captain frowned at me, but I countered with a sardonic smile.

"That's not exactly what I said."

"Well, that's what I heard," Laura said, and seemed to initiate removing her gear. I thought she seemed better at it than the night before, like she had practiced in her quarters ahead of our departure. But then she tightened back the Velcro straps and quickly and efficiently.

"Changed your mind?" I asked.

"Yeah, I want to keep it on, get the whole experience."

I knew exactly what she meant.

"Lead the way," she said to the captain.

The captain led us between the metal containers, affectionately referred to as "cans," which prompted those who lived in the containers to say, "I live in a can." I had lived in a can on my first deployment, in a building called Lancaster that was assembled with a bunch of the eight-foot-by-twenty-foot containers. Lancaster was no longer on HQ ISAF, having been disassembled some months earlier, I was told.

We ended up in a wooden box about twice the size of a can, where we were given the unclassified mission briefing with which each media visit commenced, the captain explained. No doubt the general and colonels who had flown in the lead Blackhawk this morning were getting the classified, much more interesting mission briefing. After the half hour briefing our escorts led us on a walking tour of FOB Salerno. As we stood near the southern perimeter of the base, the captain pointed south, out over a few miles of flat farmland. Well in the distance, I could see what looked like another big base of some kind.

"The airfield and FOB Chapman are about two klicks to the south," the captain said.

"FOB Chapman," I said. "That's where the seven CIA officers were killed by the suicide bomber around January first of 2010." This caused the captain to tense up.

"That's correct, sir, but we usually don't talk too much about that. It's not part of our media briefing," she said.

"The suicide bombing tragedy was widely covered in the media," I said. There was a brief beat when no one responded. "And it was portrayed fairly accurately in *Zero Dark Thirty*, the movie. I had watched the movie a few months ago. I have a strange connection to it all."

"Respectfully, sir, how do you know the details of that event?" the captain asked.

"I was on the ramp at Dover when their bodies came home."

"Really?" Laura asked.

"Just a few months before—" I stopped myself just before saying that it was just a few months before I was on the ramp with her.

"That must've been difficult," the captain said as we kept walking.

"It was a terrible day," I said.

I kept talking, perhaps boasting. I caught myself trying to impress the captain, trying to impress the journalist. I wasn't sure if that was my object, but even though it felt awkward, I kept going, carelessly forgetting about the mother who was standing next to me.

"I did ninety-nine dignified transfers at Dover, plus the seven CIA officers. Of course, there was no media coverage of that, but . . . geez, there were at least a hundred and fifty family members there, and the chief of the mission was a mother of three. Her body came off the plane first. I was standing right behind her children when the team carried her off the plane."

Now the captain and sergeant stopped, and we formed a little circle.

"I can't imagine," the captain said.

"That had to be a tough day," the sergeant said.

"They all were," I replied, and finally remembered the mother in our group. So, I tried to say something right. "Some were harder and more memorable than others," I continued, looking straight at Laura McGower, the mom who watched a metal case with her son's body come off a plane on the Dover tarmac. "But they are always hard, and I tried to treat every one with the greatest respect despite the numbers."

"And I know you did that," Laura Paige said. I nodded and whispered, "I'm sorry" and she stroked my arm, almost unnoticeably. But I noticed, and it was enough. Then there was a pause in the tour while everyone seemed to catch their breath. The captain regrouped.

"We're going to gear up and go to a shura," she said. "We're going to attend what's called the local DCC, or district community council. They're having an election to appoint the new council. Some local Afghan journalists will be covering it. We'll be going with our KLE team."

"KLE?" Laura asked.

"Oh, sorry, Key Leader Engagement," the captain said.

We marched back to the tent, and I threw my body armor over my head and tightened it against me with the numerous Velcro straps. I transferred my nine-millimeter pistol from my belt to the front of my vest and put on my helmet. Laura Paige only had to add her helmet to her ensemble, still dutifully toting the weight of the body armor like a soldier downrange. Maybe that was part of this quest too, to carry the weight and perhaps with it the burden her son had carried with some kind of twisted symbolism. We drove out of the FOB in a three-vehicle convoy, the captain and the sergeant riding ahead of us with their drivers, and Laura and I in the rear seat of the last Humvee with our own driver and gunner.

We exited the FOB and the smooth, paved perimeter road and followed a dirt road around two bodies of water that I believe were poop ponds, although I didn't really smell anything afoul, but didn't point out the ponds to Laura Paige. Then the dirt road snaked for a hundred meters and connected to a paved road. We joined the main, two-lane road, took it over in light traffic, so we had no obstructions or delays. The road was long and straight and looked like it had been built by Americans for Americans. The locals yielded to our convoy as we approached vehicles on the street or the dirt roads that entered this main road. But our drivers were not overly aggressive, just firm in their need to own and control the thoroughfare. We passed between fields and irrigated patches of farmland, across a river that looked almost dry and could've benefited from a wet spring and heavy mountain runoff. At the river crossing the road narrowed to one lane, and our drivers charged forward while the oncoming traffic yielded patiently. We passed several large compounds that looked like they were occupied by the wealthy families in the district.

Two more paved highways emptied into our road and the traffic picked up, but our drivers negotiated it without any delays, and with very little profanity. The road bore right, and I could see the airfield to my left and across the way a cluster of buildings and containers I had identified previously on an aerial map as FOB Chapman. I wondered what kind of mischief might be going on there at the moment.

In five more minutes we were in Khost city, pushing through traffic on more narrow roads now, crowded by clay buildings, cars and Afghans on bicycles and motorbikes of various types. The people were going about their business, even though this was one of the most dangerous and explosive cities in the entire country. The citizens looked undeterred, or maybe just accustomed to the occasional suicide bomber that blows himself—and American soldiers—up frequently in this volatile village.

At the first roundabout we went right and in another minute were at the gate of an expansive compound in the middle of the city. Two armed guards checked us out thoroughly. But the captain charmed him, and the uniformed Afghans pushed apart the large metal gate and welcomed our little convoy. We parked in the compound among a dozen other vehicles. The local Afghan citizens arrived, but mostly on foot. We egressed the vehicles and I stood by the back of my vehicle and awaited instructions from the captain.

"Do we ground our gear in the vehicles, or keep it on?" I asked.

"Sir, we can leave our body armor but keep your nine-millimeter on you," she said. "The drivers and gunners will stay with the vehicles."

Two more armored Humvees entered the compound after us, and four more American officers emerged from them, plus an Afghan interpreter.

At the door to the largest building we were inspected again. The Afghan National Police guards motioned in the direction of our nine millimeters, but the captain shook her head. The guards argued, and then the interpreter with the other American officers appeared magically, and he argued with the ANP guards and in seconds everything was resolved, and we passed by the smiling guards and entered a large, crowded hall filled with mostly Afghan men, plus a few women who sat segregated in a corner of the room.

"What are we here to see?" Laura Paige asked the captain.

"This is the election to seat a new district community council, or DCC," she explained. "This is democracy at the local level."

Then suddenly, the meeting was underway. We were still standing at the back of the hall, the two American officers in front and the interpreter sandwiched between them and my little group,

Laura McGower, me, the captain, and the sergeant. I looked at my watch at it was 10:48 a.m., and I wasn't sure if the meeting was starting early or late. The leader of the group began to speak loudly and fast, and our interpreter began to whisper in English, capturing most of what was being said, I think.

"He said, 'we are taking care of small disputes over land, or other kinds of property,'" the interpreter said. "'like payment issues, small cases, and we are doing this within the laws of the government.'"

Laura Paige started writing notes as fast as she could. I tuned out the interpreter and just took to observing the people around me, who watched and listened intently. They looked pleased with the developments of the meeting, but I had no way of being sure of that. When names were called—the council candidates I presumed—the men named stood up and the people voted by the raise of hand. Five men were seated, I think. No women were nominated.

When the voting was over and the council was elected, local TV crews pushed their way toward the newly elected council members. Our group moved forward too, with our interpreter still encircled by Americans. When the journalists started the interviews, the interpreter started whispering again.

"He says 'over the four years since this council began, twenty-seven council members have been killed, with at least half of those attributed to Taliban reprisals for council membership. Our district is located among our enemies, and they attack us from everywhere.'"

Then a different council member stepped in front of the camera and was miked up. The reporter asked the question and the interview continued. Our interpreter whispered quickly.

"He says 'elected elders who risk their lives to participate, and who don't get paid more than a fifty-dollar-a-month stipend, say that the councils, designed to provide a bridge between the local and central government, are succeeding. Doesn't matter if the international community is here or not, we are doing our jobs, the government is here for us. The government is accepting our ideas.

The councils have authority to face off against corrupt police chiefs, for example, and take their cases as high up the government chain as necessary. They also provide linkage to allow government funds to meet rural needs. Furthermore the DCCs compel representatives of otherwise warring tribes to sit down together.'"

That was the answer to one question. A long sound bite. Our interpreter barely caught his breath when the reporter asked another question and the speaker continued.

"He says," the interpreter began, using his same introduction, "my father was the council chairman when we were under Taliban control. The Taliban killed my father and because of this I joined the council. They also killed my brothers who were members of the Afghan National Police and Army. Therefore I had to continue in my father's way to bring peace to the country.'"

"Wow," I said, louder than I meant to.

When the interviews were over and the journalists were packing up, the two American officers, whose names I had still not asked or noticed, stepped forward to speak with some of the council members, taking their interpreter with them. I started to back away from the group and the captain, Laura Paige, and the sergeant followed.

We walked to our Humvees and started to gear up. I noticed many of the Afghans staring at us as they walked toward the gate.

"Those men are brave," Laura said as we stood together at the back of our Humvee and geared up. "I guess our men and women aren't the only ones risking their lives to try and help this country."

I stopped, and she noticed that I had stopped. We locked eyes but didn't speak. I wondered if she would write that. I wondered if finally she felt something that would ease her pain just a little. I knew what her mission was here, but perhaps she could tell the story of this city and its people.

Back at the FOB we ate what felt like a late lunch. I couldn't believe it was still just midday. It seemed like Laura and I had been on a multiday exodus across eastern Afghanistan, each of us in search of something. Even I began to feel I was on a quest, not sure if I was looking for answers to her questions or looking for my own answers now.

The FOB was remote, but the food was American—thick, juicy hamburgers with real American cheese, and chicken wings that didn't match those at Wing Stop in Columbia but at least resembled them. Laura Paige continued to hammer the captain with questions about the mission, the soldiers, the special forces she knew staged from the base. Then she stopped. She couldn't say how she knew special forces operated from the base, but the captain must have assumed I told her.

"Can we go on a foot patrol in the city?" she asked. The captain hesitated, and Laura continued. "I did some research about a suicide bombing that killed three Americans in the market in 2010. Can we go there?"

"I'm not sure if there are any foot patrols planned, ma'am," the captain replied. "That can be pretty dangerous."

"I know." I'm sure Laura wanted to say, 'I know all too well how dangerous it can be.' But instead, she pushed gently. "I heard those soldiers were on foot patrol collecting biometrics from men in the town who were of 'fighting age.'" She made air quotes with her hands. "I'd like to be able to write about why that mission is important enough that American soldiers are willing to risk their lives to perform it. What's so important about collecting biometrics?"

"It's done for a number of reasons," the sergeant chimed in.

"What are they?" Laura Paige asked.

"To help the ANA vet their new recruits for one," he said.

"But it's really done to see if any biometrics match terrorists that you've killed, right? So you can see if a relative of a confirmed terrorist is walking around the town, right?"

"That might be one use," the captain said.

"I'd really like to go on that foot patrol. I'd like to see how American soldiers convince Afghan young adults to submit to biometrics collection."

Instead, she had to settle for more briefings. I slipped away from the group, borrowed a satellite phone, and looked up a number in my notes that I had never called before. The phone rang twice before she answered.

"Hello," came a groggy voice on the other end.

"Hey there," I said casually.

"Who's this?"

"Who do you think it is? Brist."

"Are you fucking kidding me? Do you know what time it is?"

"About one in the afternoon, I think."

Monika's voiced sharpened wildly. "No asshole! Not your time! My time!"

"Oh, your time," I said. I tapped my watch and did the math. "About four in the morning, if I had to guess."

"That's right. It's 4:30 a.m. What's so fucking important?"

"Uh, just wanted to let you know your journalist friend is here."

"Oh good, she made it. How long did it take you to recognize her?"

"Not long. She has no business here. I can't believe you set this up." Then, not quite as calm as I wanted: "You lied to me."

"She's a journalist."

"You lied to me."

"I didn't lie. She's a journalist."

"She's a grieving mother! A Gold Star mother." I hesitated. "I know a Gold Star mother when I see one."

"She's a journalist now. And she wanted to come to the place where her son died. She wants to know what he died for."

"Every Gold Star mother wants to know that."

"Well, she's determined to find some answers," she rejoined.

"I know that, too. I was on the ramp with her at Dover. She interrogated me a minute after they put her son's body in the truck."

She didn't fire back, and I thought maybe she had gone back to sleep.

"You lied to me," I added.

"It was the only way she could get there. And she's your problem now. Do your fucking job."

She hung up before I could deliver a sharp comeback, some kind of threat about how she could lose her job if senior leaders found out how she had twisted the facts to get Laura McGower into Afghanistan and onto that helicopter.

After the briefing, we drove to a live-fire range ten kilometers from the base, where American advisers were teaching Afghan National Army soldiers how to fire the mounted 50-cal. The adviser set up targets two hundred meters away, at the foot of a small mountain. The Afghan soldiers then wailed away, hitting the targets occasionally.

We reached the FOB by dark, visited the morale tent and watched American soldiers shoot pool and play ping-pong and video games, like college students on their weekend break. After dinner, Laura insisted on retiring early, so we went to the tent at eight in the evening and she cranked up her notebook computer and started to type at a rapid pace. Later, she stopped typing and reclined on her cot. We kept the dim, single-bulb light on. We lay there, side by side, enveloped in our sleeping bags. I stayed awake for a long time thinking about this, how under normal circumstances this arrangement would've been ill-advised, forbidden, maybe even tempting. But in war, it didn't seem so unusual to be sharing a tent with a woman who wasn't my wife, mother, or sister, just she and I, bound by the war zone. We were both volunteers. I had volunteered for this deployment; she had volunteered to come here, masquerading as a journalist, to write about this war zone, and try to make sense of this chaos for her readers. But she had really come here as a mother.

"I appreciate you doing this," she said in a tone just above a whisper. It was the middle of the night. I was not close to sleep.

"No problem."

"I don't believe that. It took the generals six days to make a decision, so it must've been some problem."

"I don't know anything about that, ma'am. I was just told you're a big-shot journalist and I was to escort you to Khost."

There was silence and I thought she had fallen asleep. "Sorry," she said after five minutes.

I didn't acknowledge her apology. I didn't really know why she was apologizing. She certainly didn't owe me an apology. She was here to do a job. Monika Winters said she was someone important and that I was to take good care of her. She was certainly important. She was more important than any journalist I had ever escorted on a media engagement.

"I thought I was looking for answers," she said, breaking a short, deep silence. "I was desperate to find answers for myself, for my daughter. But what about my son? Why was it so important for him to come here? He embraced the mission here? I can't even understand it. Why was it so important to him that he gave up his life for this?"

"I wish I knew. I barely understand my own job. I can't begin to imagine what motivated him. I wish I could understand that myself."

I barely slept, and I'm sure she didn't sleep much either.

CHAPTER NINE

I NORMALLY SLEPT light, but in a combat zone, sharing a tent with an attractive woman I barely knew, who was not my wife, her cot decidedly close to mine, I don't know how I slept at all. But somehow, I did sleep, in quick bursts. I knew I was asleep because I dreamed, then I was awake. The cycle frustrated me. During one of my awake spells, I thought that perhaps I should reach over and touch her leg, just to make sure she was still in the cot next to me. Surely, under the circumstances she would understand the reason, that it wasn't an inappropriate advance but just a cautionary stroke. But just when I felt emboldened, I heard shallow breathing, so I relaxed and closed my eyes. An hour later, I was awake again, the same thoughts swirling in my head. After three or four of these catnaps, I allowed myself a quick glance at my illuminated watch. Only a few minutes after midnight. That didn't seem possible, but darkness had rolled in around six and we were in our cots by nine, so the night would be long. I closed my eyes, and this time, at some point, I must have fallen into a deep, profound sleep.

When I woke up again and checked my watch, it was after three. This time I did not hear her breathing, so I did reach for a spot on her cot at about mid-calf. I didn't feel her calf. I didn't feel anything but an empty sleeping bag. I sprung into a sitting position, kicked out of my sleeping bag, and reached farther. Laura McGower was most definitely not in her cot!

But I tried to remain calm. There were plenty of solid, legitimate reasons for her not to be on her cot; I just couldn't think of even one at the moment. I crawled out of my sleeping bag and put on my shirt, then struggled to find my flashlight. The pointed light did not illuminate the open space of the tent, so I directed the light to the corners, to the other cots, to empty spaces where I thought she might've escaped just to find some solitude, where she could withstand all the emotional darts that must have pierced her during the long previous day.

I pulled on my boots, tucked in my T-shirt, and threw on my uniform shirt. I started toward the tent exit, then stopped, thought for a moment, went back for my ISAF identification badge. Outside I checked around the tent, then behind it, where I had actually urinated privately a few hours earlier because I didn't want to walk all the way to the latrine on the perimeter of the camp. Surely Laura was not that audacious, nor that lazy or immodest enough to squat in the dark corner behind the tents. That gave me courage, so I set off across the camp hoping the whole ordeal would be resolved by an embarrassing encroachment on her private and risky midnight trek to the female ablution container a hundred meters away. I walked quickly. Two American soldiers sitting on a picnic table smoking stood up as I approached them.

"Did you see the American woman?" I asked. "Civilian."

"I saw her walking toward the main entrance," the tallest of the two soldiers said.

"In the middle of the night?" I asked, mostly to myself. They didn't answer. "Fuck!" I yelled aloud, then "Damn you, Laura McGower. That was my first f-bomb in months." I had almost completely broken that terrible habit.

I charged toward the main entrance where I surprised a young, female specialist.

"Can I help you, sir?"

"Did you see a civilian woman around here?"

"She walked out the gate, sir," the specialist said, much too calmly.

"What?"

"I asked her what she was doing, and she said a convoy from

Chapman was coming for her. Sounded strange, but I figured she knew what she was talking about."

"Fuck!" That was the second.

I passed her and walked twenty feet beyond the checkpoint, looked along the wall, the area well-lit by tall lights that illuminated the wall and created a safety zone beyond it. I saw nothing and returned to the specialist.

"When was that?" I asked.

"Sir, at least an hour ago, maybe more. I've been on since midnight and my sergeant has been by several times to check with me."

"Did you tell your sergeant about this?" I wanted to be angry, but she was twenty years old, standing sentry at the gate of an oft-attacked FOB in Afghanistan. She was too brave for me to doubt her.

"No sir."

"Didn't you think it was odd that a woman walked out of the FOB by herself in the middle of the night?"

She started to look worried now, like being on the receiving end of an ass-chewing. But that's not what this was. In fact, I was remarkably calm, too stunned to even comprehend what was happening. If something happened to Laura Paige Hatfield, it would be the end of my career, not a twenty-year-old spec 4.

"Sir, I guess so, but she said a convoy was picking her up."

"Did you see a convoy pick her up?"

"I don't think so, sir, but she walked around the corner, out of my line of sight."

Before Afghanistan I was somewhat of a novice gun handler, but that had all changed with training and six months in the combat zone. Without thinking about it, I pulled my nine-millimeter and charged the handle to chamber a round, released the safety, and lowered the weapon by my side, then walked down the wall. Without my glasses I could barely see fifty feet in front of me.

"Fuck," I said again. The lack of visibility infuriated me, but now I was more concerned about her life, and mine. I walked nearly out of the light and called out her name in a loud whisper. No response, no movement. Nothing.

Inside me, panic was setting in. But on the outside, I tried to stay calm. I walked quickly back past the checkpoint, then to our tent, hoping she had somehow doubled-back behind me and returned to the tent. Not a chance. The tent was empty and cold, dim from the single light bulb. Emboldened now by growing anger and desperation, I sat down on my cot, leaned across to her cot, and started digging through her gear, undeterred by the personals I might come across. I rummaged through her backpack, pushed aside her spare panties and socks, until I put my hands on a folder of some kind, and slid it out of the pack and opened it just below my flashlight. The first document I saw in her folder was a redacted AR 15-6, the Army's investigation into the suicide attack that had killed three US Marines back in 2010. One of those marines was Lance Corporal Ryan McGower of the Marine Special Operations Command. I studied the storyboard—normally classified—and my eyes were drawn to some highlighted numbers—GPS coordinates, and I knew if I followed those coordinates exactly where they would take me. Then I remembered, from the day before, seeing her sophisticated GPS and given no serious thought to her clever reply, "just in case I get lost out here."

I folded up the storyboard and stuffed it into my uniform pocket, ransacked my own gear to find my green government-issued notebook until I found the cell phone number and hooch location of the sergeant who had escorted us all day, but had not said much. I walked back out into the chilly night and started the search for the container that matched his number. At the same time, I called his cell phone. A groggy voice came on the line.

"Yeah."

"Master Sergeant, this is Lieutenant Colonel Watson."

"Who?"

"Watson, from ISAF. I'm here with the journalist, Laura

McGower." I didn't even realize my mistake with her name, but he was too bewildered to correct me.

"Yeah, yeah, yeah, Colonel Watson. Sir, is something wrong?"

"Yes. I need to speak with you and the captain immediately. I'm standing outside your hooch."

"I'll be right there, sir." He was noticeably coherent now, and surprisingly cooperative in his tone, despite the middle-of-the-night provocation.

The captain showed up five minutes later, in her PT gear.

"What's wrong, sir?"

"She went into the city," I said calmly.

"Who?"

"The journalist, Laura Paige Hatfield."

"What?" the captain asked.

"No fucking way!" said the sergeant in an ominous, under-his-breath exclamation. The captain was calmer, or in shock, perhaps. "Sir, what makes you think that? Maybe she's just lost somewhere on the camp."

"The gate guard said she walked out," I said, formulating a plan in my mind as to how I would explain this tall tale. "The guard said the woman told her she was being picked up by a convoy. I checked her gear. She has a storyboard from a suicide attack that happened a few years ago. She has a GPS and coordinates."

The captain looked at me, perplexed, stunned. This was certainly a situation she had not encountered. "Sir, I just don't know what to say," she said. "What do we do?"

"We have to put together a security team and go look for her."

"Sir, she's a fucking journo," the sergeant busted in. "She broke protocol. She's on her own now."

I hesitated, but only for a few seconds, then braced myself. Was I about to come across as a liar for not having a conversation with them earlier?

"She's not a journalist. Well, she is a journalist, or some kind of feature writer. But she's not just your every day, run-of-the-mill reporter."

The sergeant beat the captain to the next question.

"Sir, what are you talking about?"

"She's his mother."

The captain jumped back in. "She's whose mother, sir?"

"Lance Corporal Ryan McGower, United States Marine Corps. He was killed in the market attack in Khost city back in February 2010."

There was a short—although it seemed very long—stunned silence. "You are fucking kidding me, sir," the sergeant said.

"Nope, Sergeant, I'm not. Do I look like the kind of dude who gets up in the middle of the night at a dangerous FOB and makes jokes?" It was a long response that could've been handled with a couple of words.

"No, you don't, sir," answered the captain.

"I'll explain the whole thing later. You deserve a full explanation," I assured them. "But right now, we have to go find her. If you don't want to go, provide me a vehicle and I'll go by myself. She's my responsibility."

"Sir, you're not going by yourself," the captain said.

"I can't order you to go with me."

"You don't have to," the master sergeant said, and stormed away.

"Where are you going?"

"To gear up," he said called without turning back to us, "and to find a couple of volunteers who are willing to risk their lives by driving through one of the most dangerous cities in Afghanistan to search for a lunatic."

In less than five minutes we were ready to move. Harley, the interpreter, was still rubbing his eyes and grumbling as we gathered beside the two Humvees and the sergeant briefed the mission. The captain took the front seat of the trail vehicle with me sitting behind, our turret gunner standing right beside me. The seat behind our driver was reserved for our prized passenger, if or when we found her. The master sergeant and his driver loaded up Harley in the lead vehicle, with an extra gunner for security in the back seat to augment the primary gunner seated in the turret. Inside my Humvee it was dark, and cold, and loud. Actually, silent and loud at the same time, until the captain finally yelled above the fray. "What if we don't find her, sir?"

"Then I'll probably get court-martialed."

"Sir, you can't be responsible for a journalist who puts her life, and our lives, in danger needlessly. Whatever her mission is, this was stupidity, plain and simple."

"Yeah, I know. But I was on the ramp with her at Dover. I saw how her daughter reacted when she saw her brother's body loaded into that van and hauled to the mortuary. This woman is on a quest."

"She must have arranged for a private driver. I'm not sure how. There's no way she walked into the city."

"Maybe. I just don't know. She kept it all pretty quiet, obviously."

"Yes, sir."

The road was deserted, and the route was dark and gloomy. It looked much different from our drive along this same thoroughfare during the previous day.

"I should've gone by myself," I said. "I had no right to order you on this mission."

"Sir, you didn't order us on this mission. We volunteered," said the private in the driver's seat. "That McGower kid was probably a great fucking marine. I didn't know him, but there's nothing I wouldn't do for him. If it means risking my life to find his mother, so be it." I leaned forward and spoke to the captain just inches from her ear.

"What did you tell him?"

"Just the little bit you told me, that we were going after the mother of a marine who was killed here three years ago."

While we drove, I told her the abridged version of Laura Paige's story, and my connection to it, about that dark and blustery night on the ramp at Dover, Lance Corporal McGower's solemn dignified transfer, about his devastated sister, her refusal to get on the bus, her mother's promise. I told her that I was sure at the time that I would never see Laura McGower again, that I would never come to Afghanistan again, or discover any answers to her daughter's questions. I insisted that I had known nothing about Laura McGower even being here until our helicopter was minutes from landing at the FOB, and I fervently promised the captain I had no prior knowledge of Laura McGower's plan to stage a daring midnight escape and a perilous excursion into the heart of Khost, one of the most volatile cities in Afghanistan, an insurgent haven just thirty miles from the Pakistani border.

When I had finished telling the captain all that, we were cruising into the city. We reached a checkpoint and Harley opened his door and spoke to the Afghan security officer. We moved on. The streets were dark, the town deserted. *Only the insurgents are out*, I thought, digging up the roads and emplacing IEDs. The town looked completely different from when we were here during the day, and I had no situational awareness as to our location or route. I had not been to our eventual destination, so had no indication we were there until the vehicles stopped side by side in the middle of a main downtown street, sandwiched on both sides by shops and markets that encroached on the narrow sidewalks and made the street seem crowded and deserted at the same time.

"There she is," the captain said, "exactly where you said she'd be."

"Where?"

"Straight ahead, kneeling on the sidewalk."

I strained to look across the captain's shoulder and through the dirty front windshield.

"Thank god," the captain said quietly.

"That's where her son was killed," I half stated, half questioned.

"That's where three marines were killed a few years ago," she replied. "That exact spot. Her son was one of them."

Laura McGower was kneeling, as if praying, on the dirty

sidewalk in front of a hastily shuttered shop, apparently in the exact spot where her son had been killed by a suicide bomber three years earlier. I had never been here, and I didn't have the GPS coordinates, but she did and knelt right on top of them.

"I'm getting out. Stay here," I ordered. I was the lieutenant colonel now, and this was my operation in disarray.

"Get out and pull security, Private," the captain ordered her driver.

"Stay in the vehicle," I told the private, superseding the captain's order.

I got out, but the master sergeant and his gunner were already out of their vehicles, rifles at the ready, standing on each side of their vehicle. The captain's door opened.

"Stay close to the vehicles," I said.

"Go easy on her, sir," the captain said. "She's fucked up."

"Now she's causing everyone to drop f-bombs," I said.

"First one in months," she said.

"Yeah, me too. I had all but broken the habit until tonight." I had forgotten about the profanity-laced shouting match with Monika Winters by SAT phone a few nights earlier.

I exited the vehicle, removed my nine-millimeter from the holster attached to the front of my vest, and chambered a round. The sound echoed through the streets of Khost and almost sounded like the actual gunshot.

"Nice," I mumbled under my breath. "Wake up the whole town." I moved slowly toward her. I was angry and wanted to unload on her with every step. But, I was on the dangerous streets of Khost in the middle of the night. Better to get her into the Humvee and get back to the FOB as quickly and quietly as possible. So, I took a few deep breaths on the way, but when I reached her I couldn't quite help myself. "Laura, what in the hell are you doing?" She turned quickly and faced me, still on her knees.

"I just had to come out here once before we left tomorrow. I told the captain I needed to come here."

"The captain did not think you were serious." Nothing from her. "Are you out of your mind?"

"I'm sorry. You didn't have to come out here."

"Oh really? And what do I tell people when we come back without you? 'Sorry, I let her get executed by a couple of village lunatics who don't like us?' What would I tell your daughter? I remember her at the DT. I remember how upset she was. And you were the only one who could reach her. What would she do if you didn't come home?"

I think this hit her hard, but she pushed back stubbornly. "I would've made my way back to the FOB," she said. "I got myself here."

"What if you didn't make it back? This is a dangerous place."

"Don't you think I know that? My son died here!" Her voice rose but her eyes stayed fixed on the ground where she knelt, the most dangerous spot of all.

"Let's go, Laura. Get in the Humvee, please."

She stood up but didn't walk. "You know, my son isn't the only one who died here. Three MPs from the South Carolina National Guard died right here in this same market last June."

"I know that," I said. "I'm from South Carolina. I was at the airport when their bodies came home. I saw their families, just like I saw yours when your son's body came home."

She shook her head. "I didn't know that."

"Let's go. Get in the vehicle."

Finally, she started to walk.

"A lot of innocent Afghans have died here too." I hesitated and wondered if I had said something wrong. "Enough good people have died in this market. Let's not add to the total."

"Yep, let's not."

We reached the hummer. I opened the door behind the captain's seat and Laura reluctantly climbed in. Even if she felt like her mission here was not quite complete, I wasn't giving her any more time. She had dropped to her knees on the spot where her son had died. Whether or not that would give her any comfort going forward, I didn't know at that moment, but what other Gold Star mother has done that? I hurried around to the seat behind the driver, made a circle motion with my finger high above my head and everyone retreated from their security postures and climbed into their vehicles. Inside, I wanted to get angry again, but held back.

"You can't pull another stunt like that," I said calmly, then had to raise my voice as the engines revved and we started to move out. "This isn't just about you right now. You got a bunch of other people involved. It's fucking dangerous out here. If a dozen insurgents had rolled into that market while we were standing out there exposed, I'm not sure we could've fought them off. Some of us would've died. Do you want my wife to get the same visit you got? What about my mother? She's still living. Worse than that, what about the captain here? Or this young private? You want their mothers to get that same visit you got, just so you can fulfill some kind of personal quest?"

"No! No, of course I don't!"

Some lights in town flickered now, and a couple of vehicles roll into the street. We were waking up the town. Sharp popping sounds rang out.

"Gunfire?"

"I don't know, sir, but we're not hanging around to find out," the captain said.

The private stomped on the accelerator and we raced through the streets of Khost. Soon we were out of the city and safe, and five minutes later we rolled back into camp. The private stopped the Humvee at the opening of our tent. I thought I should say something to the captain and the rest of her brave team, so I stood by the vehicle and waited for Laura Paige to walk away first. But, she didn't.

"I meant to do that on my own," she told the captain through the open back door. "I didn't mean to involve you and your team. I'm so sorry."

"It's okay, ma'am."

"No, it's not," Laura corrected. "But, it's done. So let's get some sleep." Laura Paige walked away, disappeared into the darkness, and let the flap of the tent close behind her.

"I'm sorry about that," I told the captain when she opened her door. "I just never thought she would—"

"It's not your fault, sir," she interrupted, then added. "But, I'm really not sure what to say. That was surreal."

Good word, I thought.

"Do I report that to someone? I'm sure that little excursion will not go away quietly," she added.

"Yep. I'm glad I'm going home in a few days. I'm sure I'll get a good ass-chewing on my way out the door."

"Hope that's all it is," she said.

"Me too. Anyway, thank your team for me. We'll get out of your hair in a few hours and the embed from hell will be over."

She smiled at this, closed the door and the hummers eased forward while I stood there. I looked into the beautiful, starlit sky and wondered why there had to be war, and why young superstars like Ryan McGower had to die beneath this massive, majestic sky. Inside the tent, I stumbled around in the dim light until I reached my cot and sat down on the opposite side from Laura and with my back to her. Then I heard Laura McGower start to cry. She tried hard to suppress the quiet, relentless sobs, but couldn't manage. I removed my boots and lay prone on my cot listening to her, but unable or unwilling to say or do anything to console her. I didn't have the heart or the words to help her feel better.

Daylight came quickly. I had barely slept. I rolled up my sleeping bag in silence, stuffed my gear into the backpack, geared up, loaded a magazine into my M-9. She did the same, everything except loading the magazine. She was silent too. The captain and sergeant were outside the tent at seven-thirty. We walked to breakfast with them, but no one spoke beyond the obligatory morning pleasantries. When we walked out of the DFAC and back toward our tent to gather our gear, we heard in the distance a tremendous, rolling explosion that reverberated across our camp. The captain spun around, grabbed Laura's arm, and turned her too, then released Laura and started at a brisk walk back in the direction from which we'd come."

"Follow me. Hurry!"

Laura didn't hesitate. I didn't either. I had been near enough to explosions to know when they were dangerously close, and I knew this one was off in the distance, likely in the vicinity of FOB Chapman or perhaps in the city. As we charged between tents, I lagged slightly behind, silently hoping and maybe praying that the explosion wasn't in the market, on that spot where Ryan McGower and the National Guardsmen had died, and from where we had plucked Laura McGower only a few hours earlier. She did not need that thought swirling around in her head. I didn't want her bearing the burden of *what if* regarding the rescue mission this morning, but my inner deliberation played out even further, and I didn't want Laura thinking about an innocent Afghan child's fresh blood on the ground right there at the place where she had knelt and symbolically seen her own son's blood. I knew I was overthinking this in the seconds following the blast, but scenarios played out in my mind, complete with the sights and sounds of fire and human suffering. I actually shook my head to bring myself back.

We returned to the DFAC, a hardened structure, and plopped down at one of the unoccupied tables to await instructions.

"I'll see what's going on," the captain said. "Stay here." She looked at me awkwardly, realized she had just given me an order and added a belated "sir," but I waved it off to ensure that she knew I took no offense to her providing the instructions for the entire group, including me.

No one at our table spoke while we waited. Everyone else in the DFAC ate their breakfast, chatted back and forth, went about their business as if nothing had happened. The captain came back five minutes later.

"VBIED near FOB Chapman, just as I thought," she said.

"VBIED?" Laura asked.

"Vehicle-borne IED," the sergeant said sternly. "Suicide attack."

We sat in the DFAC for an hour, before we were finally released, locked down for the day, told no helicopters were flying due to accelerated security posture in the area. The captain briefed us on the whole event, asked Laura to make it off the record, and Laura agreed. A suicide attacker had driven his car up to the main entrance of FOB Chapman and had tried to talk his way onto the base, according to the ANA guards who turned him away. When he couldn't breach the security checkpoint, he detonated a thousand pounds of explosives right in the queue of cars trying to legally access the base, killing one ANA soldier and a half dozen Afghan civilians. In a strange and twisted way, it was yet another win for the ANA, who did not allow him to breach the base perimeter.

We were sent back to our tent to pass the morning. I stretched out on my cot and tried to catch up on the sleep I had missed the night before. Out of the corner of my eye, I could see that Laura was sitting upright on the cot. That's when, for the first time since the night before, Laura and I spoke to each other.

"That could've been us last night while we cruising around Khost city in the middle of the night," she said, and waited for me to reply. But, I didn't. "And it would've been my fault, of course. Not sure how I would live with that on my conscience."

"Don't think about it. We're fine. It's an ugly war out there. And the enemy has *no conscience*."

A half hour after being told we were stuck here another day, the lockdown was lifted, and we were on the helicopter flying away from Khost city. I was glad because I didn't want to fly over the city and the market so Laura Paige would have to see the place again. We flew back into the Kabul valley late in the morning and landed on the soccer field. I had not told any of my colleagues about the delay, and apparently they were not worried about us because no one had called after the explosion at Camp Chapman. There was no welcoming party when we climbed out of the Blackhawk, lowered our heads, and scurried across the soccer field.

We arrived two hours late for an interview with General Kinkel, which had been scheduled for midmorning. I took her straight to the general's office, hoping to sway her one last time with even more perspective as she prepared to depart Afghanistan and return to America, where she would write a story about her experiences, and make a desperate attempt to provide readers and her daughter answers to those cutting questions I had heard on the Dover tarmac three years earlier, questions that still haunted me. My relationship with General Kinkel allowed me to ask him—two hours late—to sit with her for a few minutes. During the final few seconds before we entered his office, I stewed over whether to present her as a journalist or as the mother of a fallen service member. I worried that he would doubt my credibility as a public affairs officer if I admitted to him that we had let the mother of a fallen US service member talk her way into the combat zone and onto an American helicopter bound to spend two days in a dangerous Afghan city. Just moments before the interview started, I did reveal to the general her true identity, but decided not to tell Laura that I had told him. So, I sat her in the chair where I had sat other journalists and waited for the fireworks.

After an extended exchange of pleasantries—the general was at his most cordial and charming in front of an attractive American woman—he decided to try and give her some answers.

"A few months ago we went to visit the Afghan Air Force," he said. "I wanted to see for myself the potential of Afghan pilots. So we flew with a young Afghan helicopter pilot in a Russian-made helicopter. He had beside him a Czech instructor pilot. And he was tough!" the general emphasized, pounding his clinched fist into his open hand. "I wondered how the young Afghan pilot would react when faced with harsh mentorship and criticism from this instructor pilot, but the Afghan pilot accepted all the feedback and put it into his flying immediately."

Laura shook her head, and I was satisfied the general had made his point. She threw out a question quickly.

"Sir, I understand from the colonel that you are a fighter pilot in the German Air Force, and you've put your career on hold to come here for a year, correct?"

"Yes, that is correct," he said.

"Is it worth it?"

General Kinkel thought this over for a few seconds.

"When I go back to Berlin, my friends will ask me this exact question, 'was it worth it?' And I will say to them, 'yes,' that NATO and the international community gave the Afghan people hope. Now, the Afghan security forces must be able to provide their own security in the future, but we have given them a chance."

After an hour with General Kinkel, as eloquent and sincere as I had ever seen him in six months of splendid eloquence, we left his office. I had given her everything she asked for, I believed. I wondered if it was enough. I looked at my watch as we meandered through the camp, the only people casually strolling about.

"You hungry?" I asked.

"Sure. I'll buy."

"Big spender," I said, thinking of all the times I had eaten for free by simply swiping my meal card and passing another twelve-dollar expense to the American taxpayer. It was like she had read my mind.

"I'm not talking about dinner at the DFAC," she said, laughing at me. "I'll really buy."

"I don't see a Longhorn Steakhouse."

At that moment we were passing in front of the Afghan restaurant.

"This is better."

She cut an abrupt left turn in front of me and headed straight up the stairs. I entered the restaurant behind her. It was deserted except for the staff. I'm not sure how, but she effortlessly ordered two dishes—one of which was, coincidentally, my favorite—and we sat at a table in the corner to wait. The smell of simmering chicken and seared beef wafted through the restaurant. The young Afghan men laughed and talked in Dari. I was suddenly very hungry, anticipating the taste of seasoned meats folded into naan bread and dipped into eggplant sauce, and of course, the delicious Afghan rice flavored delicately with spices and carrots. Afghan food, one of many things I would miss when I departed this ancient and battered land for the last time. I'd have plenty of chances to eat at Longhorn Steakhouse in the future—and for the rest of my life—but food like this would be hard to find in South Carolina.

We looked at each other. I was too tired to talk but could sense that Laura had a lot to say. So, I waited patiently for her.

"The captain and the rest of those soldiers were impressive," she finally said.

"She and the sergeant were airmen," I corrected, but not sure why I did. It was needless, I realized quickly, but finished. "They were Air Force. The drivers and security team this morning were Army."

"Got it." She paused, thought, then continued. "I don't know what motivates young people like that to come to a place like this. It takes a special kind of person."

"Yes, it does."

A discerning look froze onto her face.

"Like my Ryan," she said. "A special person like my son, Ryan."

"He was certainly one of those special people," I said, confident in saying it without ever having met him.

"Why am I here?" she asked rhetorically. Again, I just waited. "I had to know what he died for, so I could finally tell my daughter something. I think I've found some answers. I'm not sure yet. But I think he knew why he was here, and what he was fighting for."

She paused again. The food came, and I looked up at the Afghan boy and smiled, thanked him, but didn't break her concentration. She watched the Afghan boy walk away and disappear back in the kitchen.

"Maybe I just needed to be sure that he knew why he was here, and what he was willing to die for. I think I've answered that."

We started eating. I tore my naan, placed a piece of chicken in the piece and rolled it carefully, then dipped it in the sauce.

"That's good," I said.

She started eating too, but not with the same enthusiasm as me. But I knew she wanted to talk, and I wanted to listen, and eat. So, the setting was perfect.

"And I did it for my daughter."

"Yeah, I remember her," I said through a mouthful of rice.

"I promised her."

"Promised her?"

"That's how I convinced her to get back on the bus when we were on the tarmac at Dover. She kept asking me why it had to happen. Why her brother had to die. I promised her I'd find an answer."

She kept talking and I kept listening and eating. She told me that it looked like there has been progress in Afghanistan, and that was encouraging. She talked about Ryan, and how excited he would be when there was progress, and when he could see hope blossoming around him.

"He actually told me once that if he died, he knew it would be for something," she said. "I almost ignored him, because I certainly didn't want to think about that."

"Yeah, not exactly what a mother wants to hear when her son is in a combat zone," I said.

"That's for sure."

We kept talking long after the food was gone. After an hour I knew Laura McGower better than I ever thought I would know her and knew why her son had been such a stalwart, courageous US Marine. All those compliments by his high school principal and football coach had been well-earned and deserved. Very early the next morning we drove her to the civilian side of Kabul International Airport for her flight home. I opened the back of the armored vehicle and pulled out her duffel bag, dropped it on the dirty sidewalk. She leaned in close, and I thought she was going to kiss me. And then she did, but it was innocent and quick, a little peck on the cheek that I didn't wipe off.

I looked around and hoped the sergeants had not noticed, but at the same time wanted to rub it in just a little. I was the lucky son-of-a-bitch on the receiving end of that, and any man who saw Laura Paige would have felt the same way. They didn't even clear their throats, and she didn't say anything about the kiss, but just before walking away, offered these parting words:

"I still can't believe these extraordinary young people, serving for a cause bigger than themselves," she said. She let out an uncomfortable laugh. "And I really can't believe you all risked your own lives to track me down in Khost and bring me back safely to the FOB."

I couldn't believe it either, but what the hell did she think we were going to do, just leave her out there? I was still a little pissed off about it, but after that short, sweet kiss, I didn't expect to ever bring that up again.

My NCOs, however, didn't feel the same.

"What was she talking about, you tracked her down in Khost and brought her safely back to the FOB?" Shealy asked.

"Yeah. Something like that."

CHAPTER TEN

AFTER LAURA PAIGE left, and even with Monika back in the camp, I knew there was nothing left for me to do in Afghanistan. On my second *last* night in Kabul—and I knew this time it would be my last night in Kabul, ever—General Kinkel and Colonel Marc invited me to the German national support building and wined and dined me. They ordered two large pizzas from Milano's, and we ate pizza and drank our favorite beverages—German beer for the Germans and an ice-cold bottled Coke for me. Marc got called away, so General Kinkel and I talked about what would come next for us. I was going to retire to my house on Lake Murray. He was just fifty—a few years younger than me—and owed the German air force another decade of mandatory service before he could retire his wings and hang up his uniforms. But even though he was a relatively young one-star general and a decorated fighter pilot, he wasn't sure how high he would rise or what assignments awaited him. That surprised me.

"Of everyone I met here, you and Charlie Church were my closest friends and colleagues," I said. He smiled. "A kid half my age and a German general. Who would've thought?"

"Yeah, I know," he said, then paused contemplatively. "Really, I knew right from the start that we would be friends and work together well."

I enjoyed those last few hours with him.

Later, just like four years earlier, Monika and I sat in the garden drinking coffee and hot chocolate, talking about our dreams for the future, literally. On my first *last* night in Afghanistan, I had also spent time with a German friend and colleague before meeting Monika at the Milano.

May 5, 2009
HQ ISAF, Kabul, Afghanistan

The admired and celebrated German journalist Christoph Reuter from Stern magazine called me up and asked to see me before I left. We had been together on that memorable trip to Mazar-e-Shariff and the hospital with the "twenty-beds for drug addicts." The first memory from that trip he recalled after we sat down with tea was my dust-covered face after I had ridden a short distance in the gun turret of a German armored personnel carrier. When we had reached our destination, my face and sunglasses were covered with dirt and dust. He still laughed about how goofy I had looked. He had a good sense of humor to go with his deadly serious and deeply inquisitive journalistic skills, which had helped him create numerous renowned books and stories about the wars in Afghanistan and other regions of the world.

On our second last night together, Monika's heart was still in Afghanistan while my heart was pointing homeward, to little grandchildren who would run into my arms when I made my cross-country trip to visit them all. Monika still dreamed of a peaceful and progressive Afghanistan. I just wasn't sure that was possible. I wanted to believe that, but just couldn't. I thought we were giving the people of Afghanistan a better country, or maybe the possibility of a better country. I wanted to dream bigger, but it just wasn't easy to do.

"You know you're going to miss this," she said.

"I know. I missed it when I left the first time. I counted the days during the whole deployment, but I still missed it."

"What about this time? Did you count the days?"

"Not so much. It seemed more like I *should* be here, like I was making a difference somehow."

"And did you?"

"What, make a difference?"

"Yeah."

"I think so."

"Then why don't you stay a little longer?"

"I need to get back to my wife and children, and my grandbabies. They miss their Poppy."

"Ah, that's cute. I still can't believe you're a grandfather."

"For the past ten years."

"Really? Ten years?"

"I was a grandfather when I was forty-two."

"Geez, you started young."

She yawned big and stood up. I took the hint and we started to walk. At the gate, I turned right instead of taking the more direct route to her quarters, which would've been a sharp left turn.

"Let's take the long way—since it's my last night," I said.

We walked and talked a little, and I soaked in the atmosphere one last time (or one last time again). We passed a platoon of Italians walking and laughing, then Germans, Macedonians, Dutch, and British. The Milano was hopping, the vibration of music pounding inside the building, and Spaniards, Belgians, French, even Croatians moved in and out—like they were late for a party, not like a war was going on. Maybe I wouldn't be so sure a war was being waged if I had not just returned from Khost and stood on the ground where young Americans had died.

But tonight, there was a magnificent moon. During my first deployment I counted off the days with full moons. Tonight, a full moon illuminated the entire back of the camp, just like it had six times in my previous tour here.

"It's my last full moon," I said.

She hesitated, pondering the random statement. "Yeah, I guess so."

"I noticed all six of them, used them like a calendar."

"That's odd. I've heard a lot of different methods to mark the time, but never heard of counting full moons."

"Did it on my first deployment too. My room was at the back of the camp"—I pointed in that direction—"so when the moon was full I'd walk straight toward it when I was heading back to my accommodations. I'd talk to myself, 'only three full moons to go.' Last time I was more anxious to get home. This time . . . I don't know. Maybe I'm curious. I don't know where I'm going from here."

"Like you said, your grandchildren are waiting this time," she jumped in. "I'm sure they're excited to see you."

"Hope so."

We continued our slow stroll around the camp, past the entranceway with the large HQ ISAF welcome sign. It was darker along the front of the camp than in the area around the Milano, the gym, and other popular spots. Thirty seconds later, we were standing outside Monika's building where we had parted ways with a handshake or fist pump on a few dozen previous nights.

"Might see you tomorrow morning, but we're leaving early from the soccer field," she said. "Anne's coming."

"Smedinghoff?"

"Yep. I think it's her first trip downrange."

"She'll love it," I said, smiling.

"She will, actually. She'll love getting out in towns and villages."

"I'll try to come see you off. I'm going to KAIA with the general's convoy, so I need to be close to the office."

"Yep."

"If I don't see you in the morning, we can for sure meet up back home next time you're on leave."

"I hope so. Have a great trip home."

"Be safe down there. I've never been to Zabul Province. Lots of places I wish I could've visited while I was here."

"Hey, you'll always have Khost," she said, smiling widely.

"Yep. I guess I have you to thank for that adventure."

Her big smiled lingered. I leaned in to hug her, and she reciprocated.

"Remember four years ago, in this exact same spot?"

"I do," she said.

A chill encircled us, and it wasn't just the air. It was the first time ever that I didn't feel warmth around her, except for that middle-of-the-night phone call from a month ago, when I hated her for a minute or two, but the experience with Laura Paige had melted that anger completely.

"Okay, then," I said. "I have to finish packing. Be careful down there."

"I will."

She moved close and hugged me tight, kissed me on the cheek platonically, an appropriate show of respect with a touch of affection blended in. She stomped a few steps up the stairwell and stopped, then turned back toward me.

"Hey, I never apologized for the way I acted when you called me in the middle of the night. I'm sorry."

"Don't worry about it. Things were a little tense back then."

She reached the upper landing near the door of her hooch, and this time I stopped her.

"What do you think she'll write about?"

"Well, if I was writing that article, I'd say something like this: 'Maybe not this year or next year, maybe not in our lifetime, but eventually history will recognize the good that we've done here. Too much precious blood has been spilled on this troubled ground. That doesn't just include those brave young marines like Ryan, who gave his life, but anyone willing to put their life on the line to make this world a better place.'"

"Like you," she said.

"I wouldn't put myself in that category."

"You should. I certainly do."

"I feel the same about you, then. You're the one going down range tomorrow to try and make a difference to these people."

"Thanks."

I thought it would be difficult to sleep on my last night at HQ ISAF, but I popped a melatonin and slept soundly for eight or nine straight hours. I didn't set an alarm, but an alarm was provided for me. The staccato chopping of helicopter blades pounded on my head as I turned over in bed one last time. My room was on the direct flight path of helicopters inbound to the soccer field, and low-flying choppers had become ambient noise to me, something I had figured out a way to sleep right through during my thirty-one days on night shift. But I knew when the Blackhawks lifted off the saturated soccer field on this morning that Monika was aboard one of them. For a few seconds I wished I had jumped up, thrown on my uniform and raced the short hundred meters to the soccer field to see her off and urge her again to be safe, but somehow I didn't feel like that would be appropriate, like my presence there would be too obvious. But I ignored my own silent admonition and jumped out of bed, threw on my PT gear and running shoes, and raced for the soccer field! As I ran, I listened to the sound of the aircraft, knew they were still on the ground. But then, ten seconds before I rounded the corner to bring the soccer field in view, the sound changed, and I knew exactly when they were airborne again. A few seconds later, I saw the Blackhawks lift over the buildings on the edge of the camp and disappear. I stood and listened to the murmur of rotor blades until the sound faded into the morning, replaced by the chaos and clatter of the Kabul streets beyond the walls of the headquarters. I stood erect and motionless well after the Blackhawks were out of sight and earshot and thought for the second time that I was leaving Afghanistan, never to return.

My second journey home from Afghanistan began later on that warm and bright Saturday morning, on my fifty-third birthday. I didn't tell anyone it was my birthday, even as we gathered around two convoys, the three-vehicle motorcade of General Kinkel as they prepared to depart for a local television station to give an interview. Missy Chabon hugged me first. Emmy Statler hugged me next, and we posed for a photo, me standing between her and Missy with a big smile on my face. Emmy was geared up to accompany the Germans to the local TV station for the general's interview. If I were not going to the airport in a different convoy, I would have been going with the Germans instead of Emmy.

"Do you wish you were coming with us?" Emmy asked.

I hesitated, and looked at the second convoy, which would transport our new brigadier general to KAIA North for an orientation at ISAF Joint Command. I had a reserved seat in her convoy.

"In some ways, I guess."

General Kinkel hugged me several times. Then Colonel Jack Daniels shook my hand firmly, wished me good luck and then put his mouth very close to my ear.

"I still don't know why you came here," he whispered, "so close to retirement. You did good work here, but what we do on the press desk is secondary to family. I admire you for coming here. You're a good man."

"Thank you, sir."

General Kinkel came back to me after Colonel Daniels.

"I'll never forget you. You're a true friend," he said. I felt a trace of sadness at his words because I knew that once we departed the camp today, there would be little chance we would ever meet again. That's how it was with just about everyone I had met on my first deployment—Monika Winters and a few others being rare exceptions—and I knew that's how it would be with nearly everyone I had met and come to respect and admire on this deployment. I hoped that Monika would be the rare exception again if we were able to reunite in the States later.

"I hope our paths cross again someday," I said to him quietly.

"Me too, my friend," he said, and then his team ushered their general toward the middle vehicle in his convoy and they drove away.

Even though I meant those departing words sincerely, I don't recall giving General Kinkel another thought until the next day when I started thinking back on the beginning of the end of my time in Afghanistan. And so I guess the answer to Emmy's question was really *no*, I had not wished I was going with them. Or if I was going with them, I would want it to be my choice when I got to leave.

I rode in the convoy to Kabul International Airport with the new general who had replaced General Twitty, a fellow South Carolinian who had made my life hell some days, and had been an exemplary leader, mentor, and friend on other days. Every time I was scheduled to see him or saw him unannounced, I first wondered what side of the bed he had gotten up on that morning. But that was behind me. The general had moved on to a higher command and more responsibility in the Army, well-earned, not withstanding those few memorable moments I had enjoyed with him (that was sarcasm), and I was moving to the next chapter of my life. But right here, in this moment, I tried to absorb every image, every scene as I made my last ride through Kabul.

"I made this drive four years ago and I was sure it would be the last time," I said to my drivers. "Never thought I would have a second last drive through Kabul."

"You're lucky, sir. I wish I was going with you," said the Navy petty officer in the gunner seat.

"Your time will get here soon."

I actually hoped there would be some traffic, so we would have to stop, and I could get a longer, more contemplative final look at the shops, the men sweeping the streets, the women in burkas, and the children going to school, for whom I had so much hope, but so much doubt at the same time. On one sidewalk, schoolgirls distinguishable by their black dresses and white headscarves, lined up for at least fifty feet, waiting to get into their school compound, probably going through security checks and metal detectors before they were allowed to enter. The children too poor to attend school worked on the streets, moving commodities to the markets, shacks really, but the lifeblood of the economy in the districts around KAIA.

When we reached the gate, I knew that was really the last I would ever see of Afghanistan, except the mountains in the distance, or what I would see from the air on the short flight from Kabul to Bagram. Even though I wouldn't physically leave Afghanistan for another twenty-four hours, I was really gone already.

At KAIA North I had nothing to do but visit. So I first tracked down a hometown friend who had come to Afghanistan as a government employee after the University of South Carolina had denied him tenure as a journalism professor. We had a leisurely lunch and then he showed me around his directorate and introduced me to some of his colleagues. I introduced him to the new ISAF public affairs chief who was trying to replace his deputy. My friend, who had trained for months for his assignment, but come to Afghanistan only a month earlier and at a lower pay grade than originally promised, was already considering jumping ship to the public affairs team.

I secured myself a bed for my one night at KAIA, dropped my hand-carry bags against the metal frame of my bunk and stretched out on a lumpy, worn mattress that didn't do much to cushion the springs poking through. But in an instant, I was asleep. When I woke up, I wasn't sure it was still daylight because my roommates— Germans, Brits, and Poles—had covered the windows with towels to provide some relief for day-sleepers. So, I got up and walked blindly toward the end of the room, following the light creeping under the exterior door. The light was from an unnaturally yellow bulb covered with grime. Night had fallen.

I ate dinner and then dropped in on my colleagues at the ISAF Joint Command press desk, officers and NCOs I had spoken to almost daily for six months but had never actually met face-to-face. Captain Dan Leonard didn't look anything like the young officer I had pictured in my mind after dozens of conversations with him. His eyes went straight to the name tape on my uniform.

"Hey sir, glad to finally meet you," Captain Leonard said.

"Same here. Just killing time. My flight is at zero-dark-thirty."

He looked back at his computer screens.

"What are you working?" I asked.

"Suicide attack in Zabul a few hours ago. Four US killed."

Zabul. The place went right past me for a brief moment.

"Wait. Zabul?"

"Yes, sir."

"We lost four military service members?"

"I think so. We're not sure yet."

"Damn. Never stops, does it?"

He could only shake his head, then refocused on his work. I picked up the phone and called the ISAF press desk, now desperate for more information. Lieutenant Rory Quenton answered the phone. I grilled him for information without pressuring him to mention names. Either he didn't have information yet or wasn't providing it freely, even to me, the guy who had been his boss until a few days ago. I hovered over Captain Leonard for two hours but couldn't find out any more details about the Zabul suicide attack.

I lay on my uncomfortable bunk until at least midnight before I could sleep. My cell phone alarm chimed four hours later, and I threw on my backpack and hiked to the passenger terminal. In lockdown, the wait and lack of information were excruciating. I connected to the internet and started reading news reports about the Zabul attack coming out of Kabul. Four Americans killed by a bicycle-borne suicide bomber who might've been targeting an Afghan leader unassociated with the American convoy. That was it. No more news. I tried to put out of my mind all the speculative thoughts as I boarded the flight to Bagram, on the same type aircraft, Dash 8-100 STOL (short takeoff and landing) I had flown from Bagram to KAIA almost six months earlier with Captain John

Callahan, back when I was anxious, and even excited, to reach Kabul and HQ ISAF for the second time. That now seemed very long ago.

I was on the ground at Bagram for eight long hours, so I took another photo in front of the Pat Tillman USO, just like I had done four years earlier. I still couldn't get news about Zabul, and Monika was not responding to Facebook messages. I knew that didn't mean anything but seeing a few words from her would've been comforting.

From Bagram we flew on a C-17, arriving at Manas Air Base, Kyrgyzstan—my fourth time landing there—late in the evening on a Sunday night. When my weapons case was loaded on the pallet for BWI, and my chemical warfare protection, body armor, and helmet were turned in, I felt the load become considerably lighter. We were treated to the Manas tradition, briefings and equipment turn-in before food or sleep, so finally, at two in the morning, I slept, again on a springy mattress in a large tent with fifty of my closest friends.

It was after ten the next morning when I pulled myself up from the bunk, my back burning with pain and tightness. In six months I had taken two days off. This was the third day in the past six months I had nothing to do, really, but I had to know about Zabul. That was my first thought when I rolled out of my bunk on my first morning at Manas, my fourth and last transit through this base. I took my iPad to the recreation center and started searching. Finally, I picked up the phone and started calling back to the ISAF press desk. Emmy Statler put me on hold. After a long, long wait, Major Peter Bryant's voice took over.

"Hey sir. It's Pete."

"What's up?"

"Busy, as you might expect. How ya' doin'?"

"Bored."

"I bet. Not here."

"Yeah, I heard," I said.

There was a long pause, and now I knew the news would not be good. So, I beat him to it.

"Are y'all releasing the names of the casualties from the Zabul attack?"

He cleared his throat.

"Not yet. I only know about Mr. Karima. He was injured, but the colonel said he's going to make it."

Karima was one of our Afghan American translators and cultural advisors. He had recently gotten a key position at the US Embassy. He was overwhelmed by that new opportunity and responsibility. I experienced a quick flashback of an earlier meeting with him, a rehearsed, subtle, and diplomatically delivered admonishment on how we should work with the other Afghan Americans in our office, who were contractors, not federal employees.

"So he's okay?"

"Yeah. Colonel Daniels talked to him and he's going to be all right," he said.

With this unnerving lack of information and certainty, I tossed and turned until after three o'clock, and then it was time to check in at the passenger terminal for lockdown. I was wide awake. Four scheduled hours in lockdown turned into three, which seemed to go by remarkably fast considering the many hours and vast distance that formed a long, wide space between Manas and Columbia, South Carolina, where my wife would rejoin my life, and some of my children and grandchildren would welcome me.

The sun broke over the eastern horizon as our commercial airliner rose from Manas airfield and over Kyrgyzstan. Once airborne, I looked out of my window at the gray, barren country below, flat farmland ringed by tall, sharp mountains in the distance. In minutes we were over the clouds and the ground below disappeared for hours. Inside the airplane, before the movies started, the aircrew displayed a map on the large video monitors mounted at the front of each section of the plane. A small, airplane-type image moved slowly across the map, turned sharply north to fly around Uzbekistan and into Kazakhstan. It took several hours to fly across the vast, barren former Soviet republics of central Asia, but by the time we reached the Caspian Sea, the clouds had dispersed, and the deep, flat sea was visible below. The next land visible was Azerbaijan, and then a piece of Armenia, just north of Iran, and then into Turkey. We took a different route than my first return trip four years earlier. Instead of crossing Turkey and then flying north across the Black Sea, we flew west and slightly south, skirting just above volatile Syria and toward the ancient Turkish city of Adana and its heavily Americanized tenant, Incirlik Air Base.

It seemed like the short stop at Incirlik went on and on. The number of passengers who wanted to fly Space A (space available) to Germany far exceeded the number of seats on the flight, and the Air Force clerks at the terminal sorted through the list carefully, handing out boarding passes in accordance with each person's status on the priority list. At the top of the list were families actually moving from Turkey to Germany on official orders, and a young woman on emergency leave trying to reach the States after a death in her family. I didn't hear the details. There were families going to Germany for vacation—midway down the priority list, but ahead of the retirees hopscotching across Europe with plenty of time to sit in terminals and wait for their name to be called for a flight. There was an assortment of young daughters of Air Force families heading for a softball tournament in the Netherlands.

I couldn't make a Wi-Fi connection. No internet. No news. But I somehow managed to muster some patience, until finally we were directed to queue up and reboard. I somehow managed to get my same seat even though we had added a hundred or so passengers.

The launch out of Incirlik seemed so much different. Once airborne, Adana spread out across a flat landscape and wrapped itself around an assortment of lakes and rivers, then mountains and deserts and mountains again, until the Black Sea seemed to engulf us for the longest time. Somehow, I dozed off—a chronic bad sleeper on aircraft—and when I awoke, we were touching down at Ramstein.

The passengers in our aircraft emptied into a long jetway that twisted and turned until it connected to the terminal. I stood at the large windows and watched a C-17 taxi onto the tarmac and park adjacent to our plane. The passengers marched from the back ramp of the C-17, enlisted aircrew, a pilot, two men in civilian clothes. A cadre of support personnel hurried onto the aircraft. As the passengers walked across the tarmac toward a door on the level below where I stood, one of the faces began to look familiar to me. Just then I knew who they were, why they were on that plane, and who had been left behind on the C-17.

I walked up to one person I knew and caught him completely off guard.

"Mike Stepp," I said from beside him. He turned abruptly.

"Bristow." He hesitated and searched for his next words. He looked exhausted. "I didn't expect to see you. What are you doing here?"

"On my way home. You?"

"You heard about Anne—and Monika?"

That is how I heard that Anne Smedinghoff had been killed in the Zabul suicide attack. I had only met her a few times, but I knew from those brief meetings that her family, our country, and the entire world had suffered a devastating loss. Then my mind filled up with images of Monika, an idealist who wanted so badly to believe that the people of Afghanistan—and especially the oft-oppressed girls and women of Afghanistan—could someday live in peace. I don't know how long it took for me to come out of the fog I was in, but Mike gave me a long time to come back and waited for me to break the awkward pause.

"What about Monika? Is she . . .?"

"Monika's still on the plane."

I wasn't hearing him, and he wasn't hearing me.

"On the plane, with Anne?"

"Yeah, I'm afraid so."

It was in that moment I thought that my dear friend Monika Winters had also sacrificed her life to serve the people of Afghanistan.

It was news I didn't know how to bear. Mike Stepp moved away from me, and I stood alone in the middle of the tarmac. My pulse raced. I didn't know what to do next, but I had to know for sure. I walked slowly toward the C-17, my heart pounding, sweat starting to puddle inside my T-shirt and uniform. I paid no attention to the routine flightline restricted areas, solid red lines, and entry control points. I walked to the back of the aircraft, peered in, then marched reluctantly up the loading ramp and into the large belly of the C-17.

I froze when I saw her, slumped down beside one of the flag-draped transfer cases. My knees buckled, and I almost went down too. I wondered how long she had been there. Surely the loadmaster had not allowed Monika to sit in vigil during the landing. I waited, and waited, and finally she looked up, struggled to her feet, and buried herself in my arms. I held her tight, feeling convulsions pass through her body, realizing how close I had been to losing her—how close the world had come to losing her, and I had not yet heard what she had experienced in Zabul and just how close she had been to dying beside her friend and those American soldiers.

"I was supposed to be with Anne," she sobbed. "But they wanted me in the lead vehicle. So I changed vehicles at the last minute. Anne and some others were on foot, but I stayed in my vehicle. The explosion was horrific. I just…"

I held on and allowed her to let out two days of intense, near-death emotion that had struck so close. The brave and determined Monika Winters had insisted she travel with the transfer cases that carried the bodies of the Americans who didn't survive the Zabul attack.

"Will you fly to Dover with me?"

"I'm not sure I can."

"Can you check?"

I left her and went looking for the ground crews managing the manifests for both flights. It wasn't difficult to convince a sergeant and then a captain to transfer me from the commercial airliner manifest to the C-17 manifest. The aircraft commander, another captain, was happy to have someone on board familiar with what would happen on the ground at Dover. Monika barely spoke on the first five hours of the flight, sleeping restlessly stretched out across the canvas net seating. Toward the end of the flight, she finally talked, and I realized why she was on the plane, not only to honor her friend, but because she needed to escape from Afghanistan after the attack.

When the C-17 landed at Dover, I was suddenly very nervous and unsure about what to do or what my role should be. I had no official role. I knew that. During the previous one hundred times I had been on this ramp, my role and responsibilities were so clearly defined and standardized. But I had no status today. I wasn't family. I wasn't the responsible PAO. My rank as the senior military officer aboard the aircraft gave me some status while we were airborne, but once on the ground, colonels and generals and top civilian officials would far outrank my black cloverleafs.

When the aircraft stopped and the wheels were chocked, I knew exactly where we were and how the aircraft would be situated on the tarmac, even though I couldn't see out. The back ramp started down, the front crew door dropped open, and the DT team boarded the plane and went straight to work. I stood aside and watched, trying to stay out of the way and not assert myself in any way. But I was the ranking officer on the aircraft, so the DT officer—another sharp young captain—deferred to me anyway.

"Sir, are you the escort officer?"

"No." I pointed to Mike Stepp and two other military officers who were also standing out of the way and didn't really know what to do.

"Just catching a ride home, huh sir?"

"I was on my way home on the rotator, but I ran into a colleague in Germany, so I jumped on this aircraft at Ramstein."

"Understand, sir."

"I was here about three years ago as the PAO, so I've done about a hundred DTs."

"Oh geez. Again, I'm sorry to hear that. So you know your way around then."

"Yeah, I guess so."

Monika and I eventually made our way off the aircraft and onto the ramp, where we stood in the approximate location where the media would assemble, if any were invited. Just like every other DT I had supported, preparations seemed to take a long time. But after what I thought was about twenty minutes—I had not checked my watch since touchdown—the transfer cases were ready, the DT officer contacted the Center for Families of the Fallen, and the family bus started rolling. It arrived a minute later. The family viewing area was set up—marked by shiny silver stanchions and blue ropes—but there was no media on the ramp, and therefore, no PAO on the ramp, so I martialed the bus into its parking place like I had done dozens of times before. When the bus was in place and the family members on the ramp, I stood in my familiar place, just off the nose of the bus and what would've been as a barrier between the family and the media.

The families exited the bus slowly. Mike Stepp met Anne Smedinghoff's parents immediately.

"Anne's parents look devastated," Monika whispered.

"I'm sure they are."

I had experienced this so many times—right at ninety-nine, I remembered—and had looked into the faces of families and listened to their uncontrollable anguish. And then it hit me—number one hundred on the dot when the Air Force carry team moved the transfer case containing Anne Smedinghoff's remains down the ramp—this one felt different. With all DTs, we weren't supposed to be here. We were never supposed to be here. I was cold and numb, paralyzed in body and mind by those questions Anne's family would now ask, the question Laura Paige had asked, the question to which her daughter had demanded an answer. The question that had sent Laura Paige Hatfield to Afghanistan, where we would meet for a second time. Why? Why? Why? Why Anne Smedinghoff—twenty-five years old and so much yet to give? What did Laura Paige's son die for? What did I spend a year of my life in Afghanistan for?

In minutes, it was over. The transfer vehicle disappeared. The families were rushed back onto the bus and away. Monika and I were alone on the ramp. We talked as we made the long walk from the tarmac to the passenger terminal.

"How did you end up on that flight?"

"I asked for emergency leave. I was so close to the explosion. It should've been me," she insisted.

"It wasn't supposed to be you."

We stood motionless outside the passenger terminal. This was not the person I had walked the loop at HQ ISAF with a few nights earlier. That person was strong and hopeful, enthusiastic about hopping on that chopper the next morning for a mission down range. For a few minutes earlier this day, I had actually thought we had lost her, the scrambled words and mixed messages with Mike Stepp that I had interpreted as a confirmation of Monika's death. But while she had survived the Zabul attack, physically, something in her had certainly died there.

"I don't think I can go back," she finally said.

"You've done your share. You don't have to go back."

"I know, but—"

"You can go back if you need to, or you can not go back. It's your choice."

When I returned to South Carolina, I never went back to work, but I called my commander to confirm my retirement. So I didn't *go back* either. I resumed work on my dream house on the banks of majestic Lake Murray. I reintegrated into my large and growing family, but the ghosts of Ryan McGower, Anne Smedinghoff, Jennifer Matthews, and so many others, appeared often among us, because I couldn't get them, or Monika's broken soul, off my mind.

Sitting on my deck, looking out over the cove, I thought perhaps I would make sort of a comeback as a writer, much in the same way

Laura Paige Hatfield had. I certainly had plenty to write about. I never thought, after nearly three decades in the service and those experiences in Afghanistan and on that sad Dover tarmac, I could be satisfied sitting stoically on a rocking pontoon boat, jotting down anecdotes while waiting for the rod to bend under the weight of a legal, twenty-inch striped bass that I could fillet for dinner. I was content, but no matter how many magazine features or spec screenplays I wrote or how many big stripers I caught or rounds of golf I played, Afghanistan was always on my mind. Monika's broken heart and Anne's death haunted me. Their passion for the work and the people inspired me. After the experience with Laura Paige, whose life in Afghanistan had also changed forever, and who also harbored more than a vague CNN and Fox News understanding of the precious blood that had been spilled on the brown soil of Afghanistan, I wanted to say something.

She had already said what she wanted to say, but I was still shocked when she showed up. The double French doors from the house opened, but I didn't turn to see that it was Laura Paige, not my wife, who came through the doors and stood beside me as I watched the paint contractors putting the last coat on side railings on the eighty-foot pier that connect my shoreline gazebo to the floating dock. I heard that familiar voice before I saw her.

"I met your lovely wife."

I turned to her and jumped from my chair at the same time. We hugged, and then she handed me a magazine.

"It's an advanced copy," she said.

"When does it hit the newsstands and online?"

"Just as soon as you read it," she said.

"Prepublication approval? That's unusual."

"Nope. I just want to make sure I got it right," she said directly.

So, I started to read immediately, and we barely spoke for the next forty minutes. I brushed away a tear when I read about Anne, and I wasn't the least embarrassed to cry in front of Laura Paige.

Now, if my wife had been close by, that would've been awkward. She would've tried to understand but would not have been able to. It wasn't her fault, but she didn't know what it was like there. I had long wished that I could accurately give my wife and children a glimpse of my life in Afghanistan, but even a thousand photos and the most detailed descriptions I could write or voice just could not put a person there. I couldn't find the words to explain it to them. Laura Paige's son had lived and died there, and she had endured the rare experience of going there, and now she had found the best words I had ever read to describe the experience that was Afghanistan. The amazing Anne Smedinghoff had served and died there. Laura Paige had not met her but had done her homework and knew what an extraordinary loss Anne's death had delivered. Laura Paige had a lot to say, and God, had she said it well. I read the last few sentences aloud, in a shaky, cracking monotone.

...Every idea, good and bad, pro and con, make America the country it is. There is no other country like it. Our problems are sometimes bigger than other countries, but we are always stronger than every other country in the world. America is the only nation capable of leading the war on terror or standing up to the threats to world stability perpetuated by countries like Russia or China. But if you want to protest the president, kneel for the National Anthem, dress like a boy even if you're a girl, carry a handgun legally, worship according to the dictates of your own conscience, or park your motor home in the infield at Daytona International Speedway and drink beer for three days leading up to the race, you are free to do that. But, please remember why you're free to do that. Remember what made you free and what keeps you free. Maybe, if nothing else, the war separates the best of America from the rest of America. It gives young people like my son, and the other brave soldiers, sailors, airmen, and marines I met in Afghanistan, and amazing women like Monika Winters and Anne Smedinghoff, the rare opportunity to make a difference in the lives of Americans, and the citizens of the lands where they serve. Our warriors separate themselves from the ordinary people who just bask ignorantly and carefree in the freedom bought by precious blood voluntarily spilled in countries like Afghanistan, and in cities I will never forget, like bloody Khost. Please, my fellow Americans, don't bask ignorantly in that freedom. Honor those who make it possible. Honor those who safeguard it for you. Remember those whose lives are torn by war and conflict, and who don't enjoy the day-to-day freedoms we Americans take for granted.

By Laura Paige Hatfield
Special to American Stories magazine

When I read the last word, I looked up, thinking deeply for a few seconds. I wanted my review to roll off the tongue with the same eloquence and raw honesty as the narrative she had so painfully and beautifully told. But she was the master of words, which she had used so exquisitely to describe those heart-wrenching experiences. I was just the dude who had gotten her to Khost. So, my response to her was simple.

"You got it right," I said.

Then she wiped away a tear. No way Laura Paige had accepted her son's death, and I doubted she ever would. Maybe she had grown to understand it, and his passion for serving, and why he was so willing to die if it would make America safer and give Afghan children some hope. Maybe Laura Paige found some acceptance, even though she still struggled with it. If nothing else, I know Laura had found some answers for her troubled daughter, whose haunting image on the Dover tarmac stayed with me. Yes, perhaps they had found the answers to their questions. I wished I felt the same way. It seemed that I was still searching for my own answers, still asking myself quite frequently if my own service there had made anyone's life better. I hoped it had.

EPILOGUE

THAT WAS HOW I felt in 2013 and most days afterward, always questioning, always hopeful. In the eight years that followed, I talked a lot about Afghanistan. But I had also built my dream house on the lake, added the long pier and dock, and tied to it a fast boat. I sometimes went days without dwelling on Afghanistan, the people I met there, the experiences I had there, the hope I still felt for the country and the people. I had produced a documentary film, *Bringing the Fallen Home*, from my Dover experiences. I had interviewed dozens of Gold Star families, most of whom had lost loved ones in Afghanistan. Some had lost loved ones only weeks or a few months before I interviewed them, some had lost loved ones—husbands, fathers, sons and daughters, brothers and sisters—in years past, during my Afghanistan years and in the five or six years before I deployed there. For some, the fifteen or twenty-year anniversary of the loved one's death was fast approaching. But they never stopped hurting for what was lost, and it seemed like their tragedy stayed fresh and recent. I had forged lasting relationships in the Gold Star community, and they had reinforced my hope that we left Afghanistan better and brighter than when we had first gone there—I thought I didn't have any more to say about my experiences there and at Dover. I could just remember.

Then the news broke. It was August 2021, and President Joseph Biden directed the withdrawal of all American forces from Afghanistan, a poorly planned, politically motivated, and completely disastrous military operation that left me angry and bitter. I watched the coverage in horror day after day, with intense sadness for the people of Afghanistan, friends and colleagues from dozens of nations who had served there, and especially for all those Gold Star families I knew and the thousands more I didn't know, whose only shred of hope was believing that their loved one had died for something. In a few days, the president of the United States had snatched away that hope. I wondered about those female journalists sitting at the table when General Kinkel had asked if the glass was half-full or half-empty. They had described the glass as half-full, but envisioned a glorious day when the glass would be completely full, or at least close to it. Is there even a drop of water in that glass now, and where are those visionary journalists now? Where are those women training to be nurses at the hospital in Mazar-e-Sharif? Where are those young Afghans who came to that camp in Herat to study and share their passion for art?

Where was Baryalai Helali, Colonel Murad, and that Afghan man who had reminded me of Davy Jones from The Monkees, and the thousands of others who had fought for, and believed that their beloved country would be free. What happened to those young boys who came to that shura with their fathers in the Uzbin Valley back in 2009? Where are those shepherd boys—also grown men now—who took my bottle of water and thanked me in a language I didn't understand, and laughed at my poor attempts to communicate with them like an old-school uncle?

I wondered how Laura Paige must feel about her son's sacrifice there. What about every family who gave something or someone? Will we ever rediscover or rekindle that hope that our service in Afghanistan made a difference in the lives of the people there and to the security of our country and the world? I wasn't sure anymore. No one was sure. They were just angry and bitter, their lives shattered all over again. And that was in *this* country, where we could go to bed at night in peace, walk the streets in relative safety, and believe all kinds of things. I could only imagine what life was like in Afghanistan now.

Monika and I had lost touch, even after working together

on a documentary film and spending time at her house with my production crew. We crashed a few nights in her spare bedrooms to save the cost of expensive Northern Virginia hotels. My younger friends found her intelligent and witty, and she was enthralled with their creative talents. But our political differences had eventually driven a wedge into our friendship, and she had ignored for several years my infrequent attempts to reconnect.

I was anxious to know how the president's ill-conceived and poorly executed operation had stirred the souls of those Gold Star families and respected. So, I called Laura Paige, almost apologetically because I knew how completely her heart was shattered. "The only way to cope with Ryan's death was by holding on to hope. He made a difference. He died trying to help people. I survive knowing that. But Biden took that away from me. He took that away from all of us."

I was urged to remember that while Biden had executed the eventual withdrawal, the war in Afghanistan had shaped the administrations of the three previous presidents, and Biden claimed to be completing Trump's promised withdrawal. But, I still couldn't stop myself from believing that any of the three previous presidents would've executed the withdrawal more effectively, with more strength and resolve.

Anne Smedinghoff's father, Tom, told me an official from the State Department called him and offered an insincere advanced notice that the withdrawal was coming. What Tom was not told was how the withdrawal would be executed, and that it would be more of a surrender, that the United States would pull out its troops, and that the country would abandon Bagram Air Base and its multi-billion-dollar inventory of weapons, buildings, and every possible asset imaginable. His immediate and sharp misgivings during and after that call had been realized, and even though he had feared the worst, the withdrawal and the events in Afghanistan had been worse than he feared; all the progress made had been lost. Perhaps what angered him most was the sudden and unexpected abandonment of the American embassy in Kabul, the home base of his daughter before her tragic death back in 2013. Since 2021, he and his family have struggled—but have managed somehow—to cling to any hope that Anne died for something.

Bagram and the American Embassy. Will the next president undertake to launch a bold and dangerous military mission to take back Bagram, recover some of those military assets, or reclaim the Embassy with its billion-dollar infrastructure of offices, living quarters, dining facilities, and security apparatus? Recently, I actually had a brief conversation with General Jim Mattis, whom I had met briefly in 2013 at HQ ISAF as part of festivities related to the change of command—when General Joseph Dunford took over for General Allen, whom I had still not officially met in the five months I had worked for him. Mattis had served as secretary of defense under President Donald Trump, who had made the mistake of not accepting and acting on Mattis's sage advice, leading to the general's resignation. I thought that might be another book—*General James Mattis, One of the People Donald Trump Should've Listened To*. It was all the restraint I could muster to *not* ask Mattis how he would've executed the Afghanistan withdrawal had he still been SECDEF.

I still dream about Afghanistan, and when I do, very often an image of the devil invades every photo. Photobombing in 2023 is a comedic phenomenon that has developed and grown in our society, but when the devil photobombs your pictures, there's nothing funny about it. Every bed I slept in, every road I traveled, every town I visited is now inaccessible to me or any other American soldier. Every photo taken in Afghanistan is now darkened by the thought that I could not go to that spot now because that very spot is now occupied by the Taliban. Who occupies the room I lived in for six months at HQ ISAF? Who eats in the dining halls where I ate, the tent at Bagram where I slept awaiting my flight home, or the house in Kabul where I spent Christmas with John Coppard and his friends? What has come of the Government Media and Information

Center where I attended news conferences with NBC's Mike Taibbi or the room at Kandahar where I bunked down with another NBC correspondent, Jim Maceda, who told me it would take fifty years for Afghanistan to develop to the point where Pakistan is now. He told me that thirteen years ago. Does the clock start over now?

Since 2021, I've even dreamed I was back in Khost with Laura Paige, and she's kneeling at the spot where her son Ryan died. Then the dream turns to a nightmare when Ryan's image morphs into the image of the devil, then morphs into the image of a Taliban fighter, gripping his AK-47 and taunting the grieving mother kneeling in front of him.

Finally, I recollected often my 2012 meeting with Atia Abawi, whose heart beat to the same rhythm as the Afghan people. Her people. She was downtrodden in 2012 at the thought that we might fail in Afghanistan. I didn't have to imagine because I knew what she was feeling in 2021. She would be devastated too because her lineage, not just her heart, was tied to Afghanistan.

Well, I thought I had said or written everything I had to say or write about Afghanistan. Maybe not.

THE END

AUTHOR'S NOTE

THIS STORY IS about all the men and women of US and NATO forces who served in Afghanistan and is dedicated especially to the memory of those who didn't come home, and to their families and loved ones who stood on the Dover ramp. We should honor them every day.

This book is also dedicated to the memory of young heroes like Anne Smedinghoff, who died April 6, 2013 (on my birthday) at the age of twenty-five in Zabul Province, Afghanistan. Working as a press officer for the US Embassy in Kabul, she was helping Afghan journalists cover an event at a school where the local Provincial Reconstruction Team was donating math and science books to eager Afghan students. Other young heroes lost there include CIA officer Jennifer Matthews and her team, who gave their lives in pursuit of Osama bin Laden. I stood a few feet behind her family when her body came off the plane at Dover, and later delivered the dress her daughter had chosen for her mother to be buried in.

Most of the characters in this story are based on real people, or composites of several people I knew and worked with. I used a lot of real names, but only in cases where the events with those people actually took place as described. Laura Paige Hatfield is the only actual fictional character in the story, but she represents thousands of Gold Star families who have stood on the Dover tarmac and wished against all hope to find answers to the questions her daughter asked the night her brother's body came off the aircraft. So, there are no truly fictional characters in this story.

The fictional Foreword was written by Charlie Stadtlander, aka

Charlie Church, who served with me in Afghanistan.

I had a twenty-eight-year military career, which for the most part was unremarkable. I had a few moments, like when back in 1988 as a first lieutenant, I was named Air Force Journalist of the Year, or when I performed well as a home-base public affairs officer during Desert Storm and the many deployments of my Air National Guard unit in the aftermath of 9/11. Near the end of my career, I had thought that my most enduring contribution was writing and producing a feature-length documentary film on the storied history of the South Carolina National Guard. But then, Afghanistan happened. After my first deployment, it just didn't make sense to sit at a desk in Columbia and perform routine daily tasks as a National Guard public affairs officer. So, I volunteered for a three-month posting to the Air Force Mortuary at Dover. After four months, I had supported about a hundred dignified transfers. When I received an early retirement letter from my Air National Guard command in early 2012, I volunteered for Afghanistan again, something I had sworn I would never do after the first tour. I received a six-month extension on my retirement so I could deploy, served there another six months and retired from the Air Force and Air National Guard right after the deployment.

We produced *Bringing the Fallen Home* in 2014, but in the weeks following the 2021 surrender of Afghanistan to the Taliban, I resolved to finally shape my Afghanistan and Dover journals, notes, memories, and some fictionalized stories as well, into *This Troubled Ground*.

Les Carroll

Milton Keynes UK
Ingram Content Group UK Ltd.
UKHW010726130923
428592UK00004B/256